Bellwork®

Mathematics

Level 5

Bellwork®
educational solutions

Author
Charles W. De Pue

Co-Author
Margaret Kinney

Contributing Authors:
Kent A. De Pue
Carrie Hernandez

Editorial Consultants:
Michelle N. Barnett
Erica Kaiser

Illustrators:
José L. de la Rosa
Brenda Morales

The publisher wishes to thank the following educators who read portions of the series prior to publication for their comments and suggestions.

Rebecca Afghani	Ann DePierro	Lauren Rips
Linda Behrens	Victor Dorff	Ona L. Sandi
Pam Bluestein	Don Felton	Mindi Shapiro
Amy Brophy	Kim Fortune	Lynne Shisbey
Sue Buttera	Robin Harbeck	Ruthie Smith
Mary Johnson Cajiao	Sheri Joseph	Kim Marra Stephenson
Mark Cohen	Rebecca Keene	Kathy Terndrup
Marne Colby	Mia Lewis	Alicia Trent
Erika Daniels	Sarah Milam	Jennifer Williams
Carey Davis	Dennis Regus	

Bellwork
921 Mariner Street
Brea, CA 92821-3827

(800) 782-8869
Fax (714) 482-2379
www.bellwork.com

Printed in the U.S.A. (07/11) #31409
ISBN 978-1-932469-05-9

Name _____

❶

$$3,461 \\ + 2,523$$

Ⓐ 5,884

Ⓑ 5,984

Ⓒ 6,984

Ⓓ 5,982

Ⓔ none of these

❸ **What is the fraction that names the shaded part?**

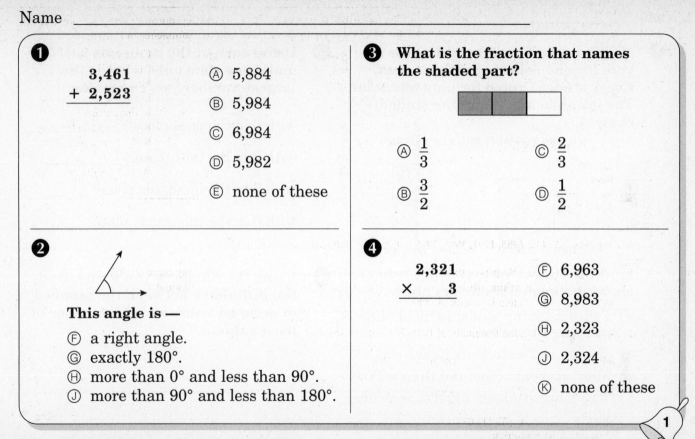

Ⓐ $\frac{1}{3}$　　Ⓒ $\frac{2}{3}$

Ⓑ $\frac{3}{2}$　　Ⓓ $\frac{1}{2}$

❷

This angle is —

Ⓕ a right angle.

Ⓖ exactly 180°.

Ⓗ more than 0° and less than 90°.

Ⓙ more than 90° and less than 180°.

❹

$$2,321 \\ \times \quad 3$$

Ⓕ 6,963

Ⓖ 8,983

Ⓗ 2,323

Ⓙ 2,324

Ⓚ none of these

❶ **Mr. Kim asked his 5th grade class to vote for one color to paint his desk. Every student voted for only one color. The graph below shows the students' choices.**

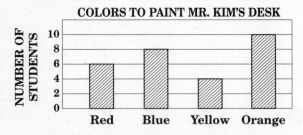

COLORS TO PAINT MR. KIM'S DESK

Find the statement that is _not_ true about the students' choices above.

Ⓐ Twice as many students liked blue compared to yellow.

Ⓑ There are 26 students in the class.

Ⓒ More students liked red than yellow.

Ⓓ Two more students liked orange over blue.

❷ **Using each of the numerals 2, 4, 5, and 6 one time only, what is the largest number you can make:**

with 6 in the ones place? _____

with 6 in the tens place? _____

with 6 in the hundreds place? _____

with 6 in the thousands place? _____

❸ **Using the numbers you wrote, find the difference between the number of greatest value and the number of least value.**

_____

2

Name _____

❶ **Gary, Anna, Jorge, and Dani are all friends. Each has a different colored bike. The colors are blue, green, red, and purple. Gary does not have a red or purple bike. Anna does not have a blue or red bike. Jorge has a blue bike. Who has the purple bike? You may use the table below to help you find the answer.**

	BLUE	GREEN	RED	PURPLE
GARY				
ANNA				
JORGE				
DANI				

_____ has the purple bike.

Name _____

❶ Which number has a 7 in the tens place?

Ⓐ 2,710   Ⓒ 1,472

Ⓑ 7,539   Ⓓ 2,607

❷

$$2\overline{)46}$$

Ⓕ 23

Ⓖ 48

Ⓗ 44

Ⓙ 33

❸

$$\begin{array}{r} 9,336 \\ -\ 7,124 \end{array}$$

Ⓐ 2,202

Ⓑ 2,460

Ⓒ 2,212

Ⓓ 2,412

❹ Juan has 340 baseball cards. Elaine has 256. How many baseball cards do they have altogether?

Ⓕ 84 cards   Ⓗ 87,040 cards

Ⓖ 596 cards   Ⓙ 590 cards

4

Name _____

❶ Find the perimeter.

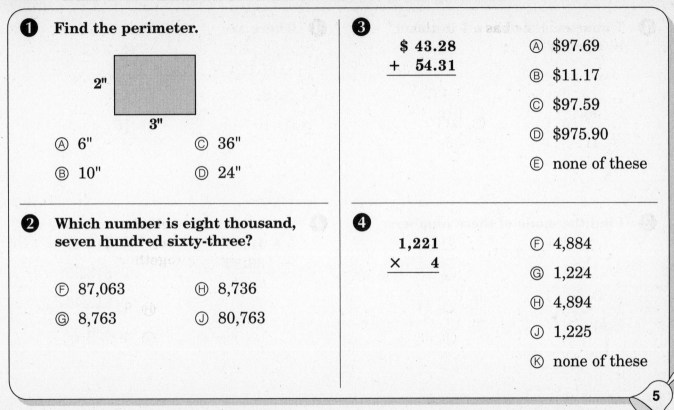

2"

3"

Ⓐ 6"   Ⓒ 36"

Ⓑ 10"   Ⓓ 24"

❷ Which number is eight thousand, seven hundred sixty-three?

Ⓕ 87,063   Ⓗ 8,736

Ⓖ 8,763   Ⓙ 80,763

❸

$ 43.28
+ 54.31

Ⓐ $97.69

Ⓑ $11.17

Ⓒ $97.59

Ⓓ $975.90

Ⓔ none of these

❹

1,221
× 4

Ⓕ 4,884

Ⓖ 1,224

Ⓗ 4,894

Ⓙ 1,225

Ⓚ none of these

Name _____

❶ **1 quarter + 2 dimes + 1 nickel + 1 penny =**

Ⓐ 46¢   Ⓒ 51¢

Ⓑ 41¢   Ⓓ 56¢

❷ **Find the mode of these numbers:**

(3, 3, 6)

Ⓕ 3   Ⓗ 6

Ⓖ 4   Ⓙ 12

❸ **There are _____ inches in a foot.**

Ⓐ 8   Ⓒ 12

Ⓑ 10   Ⓓ 16

❹

$ 49.77
−   36.32

Ⓕ $12.45

Ⓖ $12.35

Ⓗ $13.45

Ⓙ $86.09

Name _____

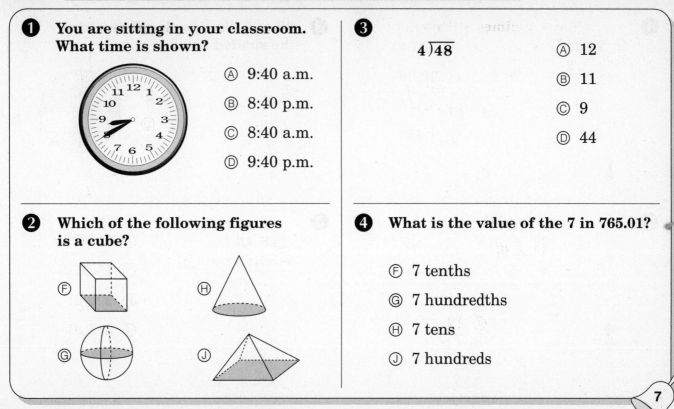

① **You are sitting in your classroom. What time is shown?**

Ⓐ 9:40 a.m.

Ⓑ 8:40 p.m.

Ⓒ 8:40 a.m.

Ⓓ 9:40 p.m.

② **Which of the following figures is a cube?**

Ⓕ

Ⓗ

Ⓖ

Ⓙ

③

$4\overline{)48}$

Ⓐ 12

Ⓑ 11

Ⓒ 9

Ⓓ 44

④ **What is the value of the 7 in 765.01?**

Ⓕ 7 tenths

Ⓖ 7 hundredths

Ⓗ 7 tens

Ⓙ 7 hundreds

Name _____

❶

$$5{,}342 \times 2$$

Ⓐ 10,644

Ⓑ 10,684

Ⓒ 5,344

Ⓓ 1,684

❷

$$27 \div 3 =$$

Ⓕ 8

Ⓗ 6

Ⓖ 9

Ⓙ 7

❸ What is the fraction that names the shaded part?

Ⓐ $\frac{7}{8}$

Ⓒ $\frac{1}{8}$

Ⓑ $\frac{3}{4}$

Ⓓ $\frac{8}{7}$

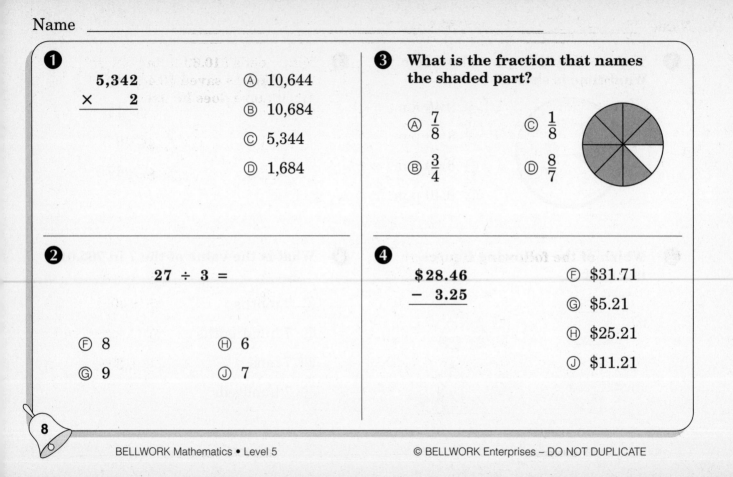

❹

$$\$28.46 - 3.25$$

Ⓕ $31.71

Ⓖ $5.21

Ⓗ $25.21

Ⓙ $11.21

8

Name _____

1

$3\overline{)37}$

Ⓐ 13

Ⓑ 12 R1

Ⓒ 11

Ⓓ 13 R1

3 Mike needs $10.60 to buy swim fins. He has saved $8.40. How much more does he need?

Ⓐ $19.00   Ⓒ $2.20

Ⓑ $12.20   Ⓓ $3.20

2 Which of the following is a prime number?

Ⓕ 4   Ⓗ 7

Ⓖ 9   Ⓙ 15

4

$$\begin{array}{r} 4{,}571 \\ +228 \\ \hline \end{array}$$

Ⓕ 4,799

Ⓖ 799

Ⓗ 4,809

Ⓙ 4,343

9

❶

$$\frac{9}{10}$$

$$-\frac{6}{10}$$

Ⓐ $\frac{3}{20}$ Ⓒ $\frac{3}{10}$

Ⓑ $\frac{15}{20}$ Ⓓ $\frac{15}{10}$

❷

$$\square \times 4 = 28$$

Ⓕ 8   Ⓗ 7

Ⓖ 9   Ⓙ 6

❸ Which sign belongs in the ◯ below?

$$4 + 8 \quad \bigcirc \quad 15 - 4$$

Ⓐ <   Ⓑ =   Ⓒ >

❹ Most people are asleep.
What time is shown?

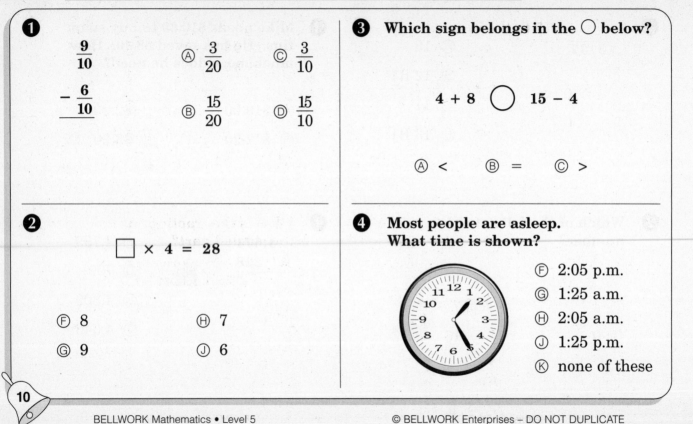

Ⓕ 2:05 p.m.

Ⓖ 1:25 a.m.

Ⓗ 2:05 a.m.

Ⓙ 1:25 p.m.

Ⓚ none of these

10

Name _____

❶ Round 1,067 to the nearest ten.

Ⓐ 1,070 　　Ⓒ 1,100

Ⓑ 1,000 　　Ⓓ 1,060

❷

6,404
× 　　8

Ⓕ 51,202

Ⓖ 48,232

Ⓗ 51,232

Ⓙ 50,424

❸

$ 28.06
+ 　9.35

Ⓐ $18.71

Ⓑ $37.41

Ⓒ $37.31

Ⓓ $27.41

❹ What is the fraction that names the shaded part?

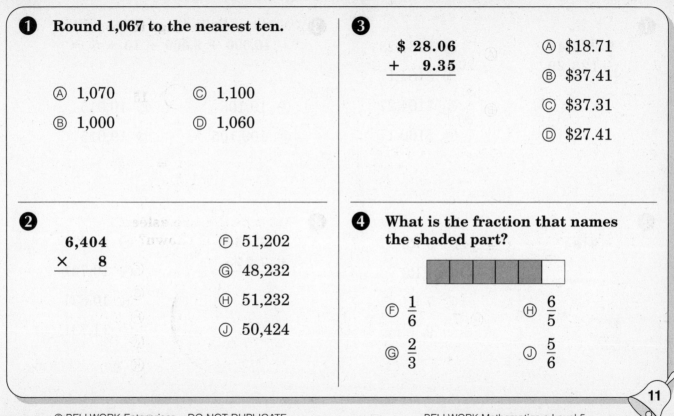

Ⓕ $\frac{1}{6}$ 　　Ⓗ $\frac{6}{5}$

Ⓖ $\frac{2}{3}$ 　　Ⓙ $\frac{5}{6}$

11

Name _____

❶

$$\begin{array}{r} \$\ 287.46 \\ -\ 123.29 \end{array}$$

Ⓐ $164.23

Ⓑ $164.17

Ⓒ $164.27

Ⓓ $160.17

❸

$$10,000 + 9,000 + 10 + 5\ =$$

Ⓐ 19,105   Ⓒ 10,915

Ⓑ 109,105   Ⓓ 19,015

❷

$9\overline{)64}$

Ⓕ 9 R3

Ⓖ 6 R9

Ⓗ 7 R1

Ⓙ 9

❹

$$\begin{array}{r} 3,456 \\ +\ 7,275 \end{array}$$

Ⓕ 10,731

Ⓖ 10,721

Ⓗ 10,631

Ⓙ 11,731

12

Name _____

❶ Use the commutative property to answer the problem below.

$$56 + 3 = 3 + \square$$

Ⓐ 59   Ⓒ 6

Ⓑ 112   Ⓓ 56

❷
$$\begin{array}{r} \$\ 315.46 \\ +\ 294.75 \\ \hline \end{array}$$

Ⓕ $610.21

Ⓖ $610.11

Ⓗ $599.22

Ⓙ $181.31

❸
$$\begin{array}{r} 24{,}364 \\ -\ 18{,}218 \\ \hline \end{array}$$

Ⓐ 6,146

Ⓑ 14,154

Ⓒ 6,156

Ⓓ 6,154

❹ The girls scored 6 runs in the first inning, 2 runs in the fifth inning, and 4 runs in the ninth inning. How many runs did the girls score in all?

Ⓕ 11 runs   Ⓗ 12 runs

Ⓖ 10 runs   Ⓙ 13 runs

13

Name _____

❶

$$\begin{array}{r} 713 \\ \times\ \ 4 \\ \hline \end{array}$$

Ⓐ 2,852

Ⓑ 2,842

Ⓒ 722

Ⓓ 2,862

❸ What is the missing number?

3, 6, _____, 12

Ⓐ 9   Ⓒ 10

Ⓑ 8   Ⓓ 11

❷

$$\begin{array}{r} 834 \\ 206 \\ +586 \\ \hline \end{array}$$

Ⓕ 1,616

Ⓖ 1,726

Ⓗ 1,516

Ⓙ 1,626

❹ Which number is three thousand, nine hundred forty?

Ⓕ 39,040   Ⓗ 30,940

Ⓖ 3,940   Ⓙ 394

❶

$$4\overline{)162}$$

Ⓐ 40

Ⓑ 400

Ⓒ 40 R2

Ⓓ 3 R7

Ⓔ none of these

❷ **Which of the drawings below shows parallel lines?**

Ⓕ

Ⓖ

Ⓗ

Ⓙ

❸ **1 quarter + 5 dimes + 2 nickels + 6 pennies =**

Ⓐ $0.96   Ⓒ $0.91

Ⓑ $0.86   Ⓓ $0.81

❹

$$\begin{array}{r} 3 \text{ hr } 6 \text{ min} \\ + 2 \text{ hr } 3 \text{ min} \\ \hline \end{array}$$

Ⓕ 1 hr 3 min   Ⓗ 6 hr 0 min

Ⓖ 5 hr 9 min   Ⓙ 5 hr 8 min

Name _____

❶

$$869$$
$$537$$
$$+246$$

Ⓐ 1,653

Ⓑ 1,652

Ⓒ 1,662

Ⓓ 1,753

❷ Which figure is a parallelogram?

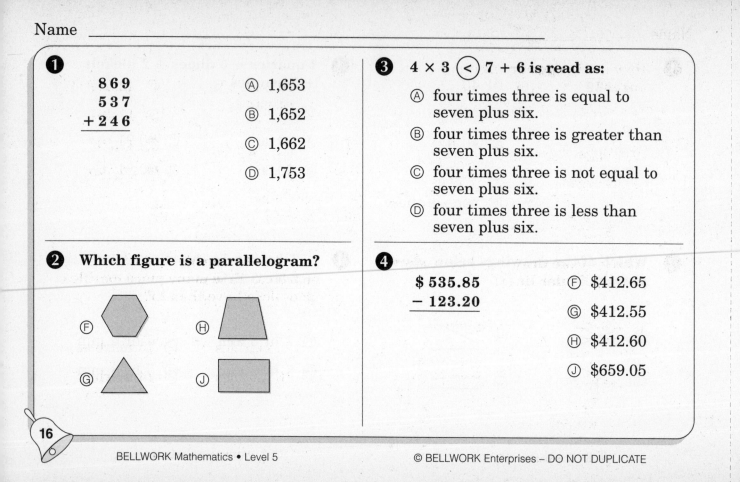

Ⓕ

Ⓖ

Ⓗ

Ⓙ

❸ 4 × 3 ⟨<⟩ 7 + 6 is read as:

Ⓐ four times three is equal to seven plus six.

Ⓑ four times three is greater than seven plus six.

Ⓒ four times three is not equal to seven plus six.

Ⓓ four times three is less than seven plus six.

❹

$$\$535.85$$
$$-123.20$$

Ⓕ $412.65

Ⓖ $412.55

Ⓗ $412.60

Ⓙ $659.05

❶ How many eggs are in one dozen?

Ⓐ 6 eggs Ⓒ 14 eggs

Ⓑ 12 eggs Ⓓ 10 eggs

❷ Which of the drawings below shows perpendicular lines?

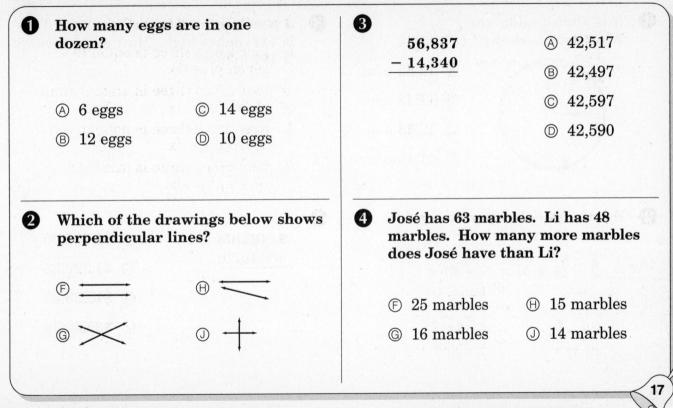

Ⓕ

Ⓗ

Ⓖ

Ⓙ

❸

$$\begin{array}{r} 56{,}837 \\ -\ 14{,}340 \end{array}$$

Ⓐ 42,517

Ⓑ 42,497

Ⓒ 42,597

Ⓓ 42,590

❹ José has 63 marbles. Li has 48 marbles. How many more marbles does José have than Li?

Ⓕ 25 marbles Ⓗ 15 marbles

Ⓖ 16 marbles Ⓙ 14 marbles

17

Name _____

1 It is almost midnight. What time is shown?

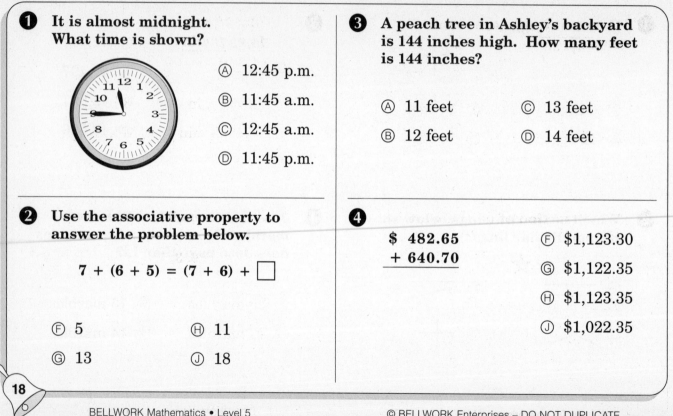

Ⓐ 12:45 p.m.

Ⓑ 11:45 a.m.

Ⓒ 12:45 a.m.

Ⓓ 11:45 p.m.

3 A peach tree in Ashley's backyard is 144 inches high. How many feet is 144 inches?

Ⓐ 11 feet   Ⓒ 13 feet

Ⓑ 12 feet   Ⓓ 14 feet

2 Use the associative property to answer the problem below.

$$7 + (6 + 5) = (7 + 6) + \Box$$

Ⓔ 5   Ⓗ 11

Ⓕ 13   Ⓘ 18

4

$$\begin{array}{r} \$ \ 482.65 \\ + \ 640.70 \\ \hline \end{array}$$

Ⓕ $1,123.30

Ⓖ $1,122.35

Ⓗ $1,123.35

Ⓘ $1,022.35

18

Name _____

❶

$5\overline{)5,725}$

Ⓐ 1,104

Ⓑ 1,145

Ⓒ 1,105

Ⓓ 1,154

❸

  7 hr 17 min
− 4 hr   8 min
_____

Ⓐ 3 hr 11 min   Ⓒ 3 hr 25 min

Ⓑ 11 hr 25 min   Ⓓ 3 hr 9 min

❷ What fraction of all the stars is shaded?

☆ ★ ★ ★

Ⓕ $\frac{1}{3}$ Ⓗ $\frac{3}{4}$

Ⓖ $\frac{1}{2}$ Ⓙ $\frac{1}{4}$

❹ What is the median of these numbers?

(6, 3, 7)

Ⓕ 8   Ⓗ 3

Ⓖ 6   Ⓙ 16

19

❶ Round 2,728 to the nearest ten.

Ⓐ 2,720   Ⓒ 2,730

Ⓑ 2,700   Ⓓ 3,000

❷ Dani has 3 boxes of candy bars with 5 bars in each box. How many candy bars does she have in all?

Ⓕ 10 candy bars   Ⓗ 20 candy bars

Ⓖ 15 candy bars   Ⓙ 8 candy bars

❸ Find the perimeter.

3 cm

7 cm

Ⓐ 10 cm   Ⓒ 20 cm

Ⓑ 21 cm   Ⓓ 42 cm

❹

$$\begin{array}{r} 4,033 \\ \times \quad 21 \\ \hline \end{array}$$

Ⓕ 12,099

Ⓖ 84,093

Ⓗ 86,693

Ⓙ 12,693

Ⓚ none of these

20

Name _____

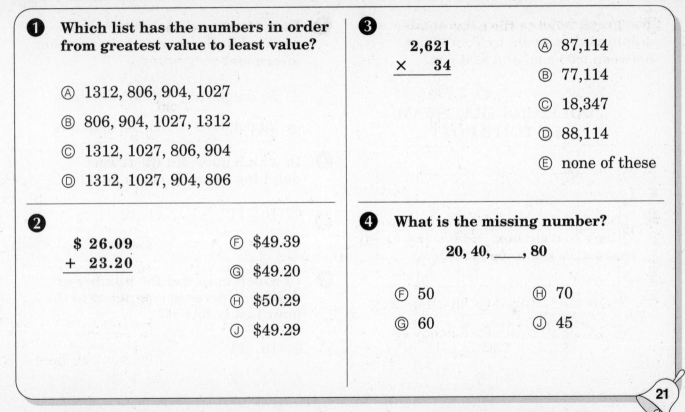

1 Which list has the numbers in order from greatest value to least value?

Ⓐ 1312, 806, 904, 1027

Ⓑ 806, 904, 1027, 1312

Ⓒ 1312, 1027, 806, 904

Ⓓ 1312, 1027, 904, 806

2

$$\begin{array}{r} \$\ 26.09 \\ +\ \ 23.20 \\ \hline \end{array}$$

Ⓕ $49.39

Ⓖ $49.20

Ⓗ $50.29

Ⓙ $49.29

3

$$\begin{array}{r} 2,621 \\ \times\ \ \ \ 34 \\ \hline \end{array}$$

Ⓐ 87,114

Ⓑ 77,114

Ⓒ 18,347

Ⓓ 88,114

Ⓔ none of these

4 What is the missing number?

20, 40, ____, 80

Ⓕ 50   Ⓗ 70

Ⓖ 60   Ⓙ 45

21

Name _____

The graph below shows the number of dolphins that swam by Tom's boat between 9:00 a.m. and 2:00 p.m.

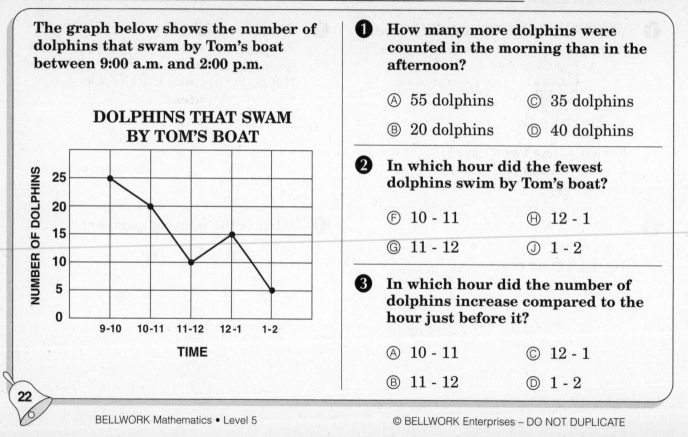

DOLPHINS THAT SWAM BY TOM'S BOAT

1 How many more dolphins were counted in the morning than in the afternoon?

Ⓐ 55 dolphins   Ⓒ 35 dolphins

Ⓑ 20 dolphins   Ⓓ 40 dolphins

2 In which hour did the fewest dolphins swim by Tom's boat?

Ⓕ 10 - 11   Ⓗ 12 - 1

Ⓖ 11 - 12   Ⓙ 1 - 2

3 In which hour did the number of dolphins increase compared to the hour just before it?

Ⓐ 10 - 11   Ⓒ 12 - 1

Ⓑ 11 - 12   Ⓓ 1 - 2

22

Name _____

❶

A **B**

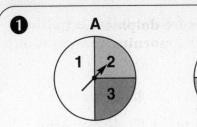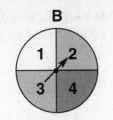

Which of the two spinners gives you the best chance of spinning the number 1?

Ⓐ A   Ⓑ B

Explain your reasoning:

❷ There are eight fish in the stream. Three bears eat all of the fish. Each bear eats at least one fish. List all of the combinations the three bears could have eaten.

23

1 If Brett reads 29 pages today and 21 pages tomorrow, how many pages will he have read?

Ⓐ 8 pages   Ⓒ 50 pages

Ⓑ 40 pages   Ⓓ 60 pages

2

$$2\overline{)10,972}$$

Ⓕ 4,586

Ⓖ 50,486

Ⓗ 5,486

Ⓙ 5,486 R1

3 Which figure below shows a radius of a circle?

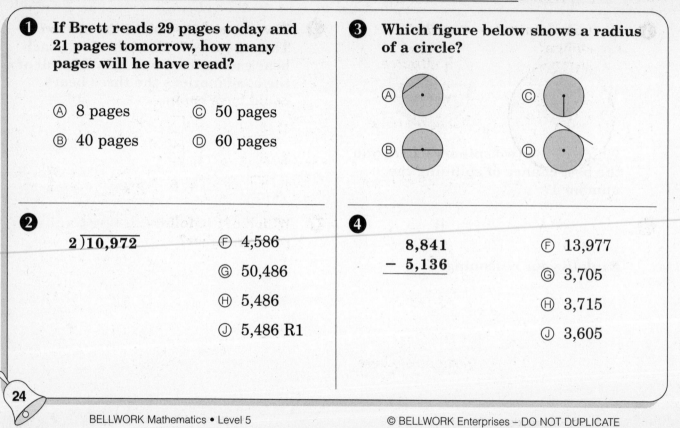

Ⓐ   Ⓒ

Ⓑ   Ⓓ

4

$$\begin{array}{r} 8,841 \\ -\ 5,136 \\ \hline \end{array}$$

Ⓕ 13,977

Ⓖ 3,705

Ⓗ 3,715

Ⓙ 3,605

24

Name _____

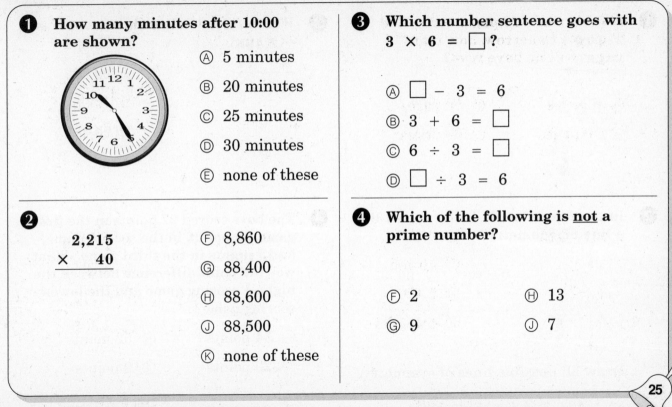

1 How many minutes after 10:00 are shown?

Ⓐ 5 minutes

Ⓑ 20 minutes

Ⓒ 25 minutes

Ⓓ 30 minutes

Ⓔ none of these

2

$$2,215 \times 40$$

Ⓕ 8,860

Ⓖ 88,400

Ⓗ 88,600

Ⓙ 88,500

Ⓚ none of these

3 Which number sentence goes with $3 \times 6 = \square$?

Ⓐ $\square - 3 = 6$

Ⓑ $3 + 6 = \square$

Ⓒ $6 \div 3 = \square$

Ⓓ $\square \div 3 = 6$

4 Which of the following is <u>not</u> a prime number?

Ⓕ 2   Ⓗ 13

Ⓖ 9   Ⓙ 7

Name _____

❶

$$600$$
$$-180$$

  Ⓐ 420

  Ⓑ 780

  Ⓒ 580

  Ⓓ 410

❸

$$2,466$$
$$\times\ \ \ \ 12$$

  Ⓐ 29,582

  Ⓑ 29,592

  Ⓒ 7,398

  Ⓓ 29,482

❷ **In the figure below, is the dotted line a line of symmetry?**

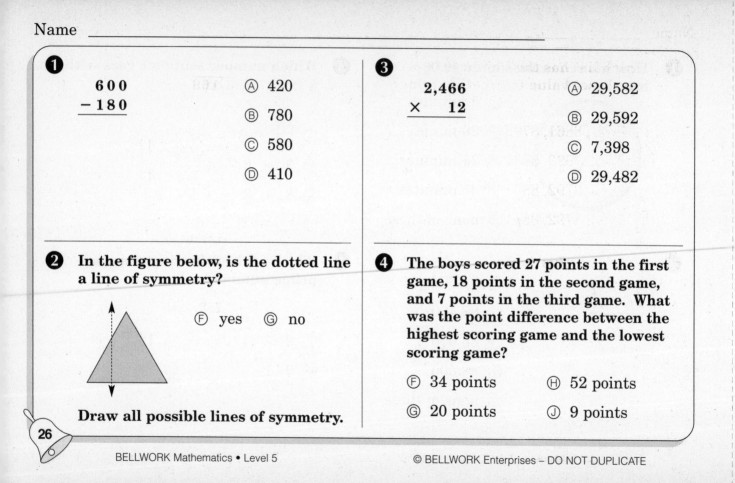

  Ⓕ yes   Ⓖ no

Draw all possible lines of symmetry.

❹ **The boys scored 27 points in the first game, 18 points in the second game, and 7 points in the third game. What was the point difference between the highest scoring game and the lowest scoring game?**

  Ⓕ 34 points   Ⓗ 52 points

  Ⓖ 20 points   Ⓙ 9 points

26

Name _____

1 Which list has the numbers in order from least value to greatest value?

Ⓐ 8841, 8861, 8792, 7993

Ⓑ 8792, 7993, 8841, 8861

Ⓒ 7993, 8792, 8841, 8861

Ⓓ 7993, 8792, 8861, 8841

2 Which number is divisible by 3?

Ⓕ 26   Ⓗ 19

Ⓖ 17   Ⓙ 27

3

$$4\overline{)168}$$

Ⓐ 402   Ⓒ 42

Ⓑ 404   Ⓓ 44

4 What is the median of these numbers?

(2, 7, 9, 3, 4)

Ⓕ 4   Ⓗ 5

Ⓖ 9   Ⓙ 7

27

Name _____

1 Which number is divisible by 5?

Ⓐ 522 Ⓒ 529

Ⓑ 145 Ⓓ 1,034

What is the divisibility rule for 5?

_____

_____

2 Which number has a 9 in the hundred thousands place?

Ⓕ 920,423 Ⓗ 309,862

Ⓖ 290,051 Ⓙ 90,150

3 Round 143,862 to the nearest hundred.

Ⓐ 144,000 Ⓒ 143,900

Ⓑ 143,800 Ⓓ 100,000

4

$$9 \times \boxed{} = 108$$

Ⓕ 11 Ⓗ 12

Ⓖ 13 Ⓙ 10

Name _____

1

$$\begin{array}{r} 4\,3 \\ \times\,2\,6 \\ \hline \end{array}$$

Ⓐ 1,218

Ⓑ 1,118

Ⓒ 1,128

Ⓓ 69

2 **Which number is divisible by 6?**

Ⓕ 30 Ⓗ 38

Ⓖ 9   Ⓙ 26

3 **Which is a right triangle?**

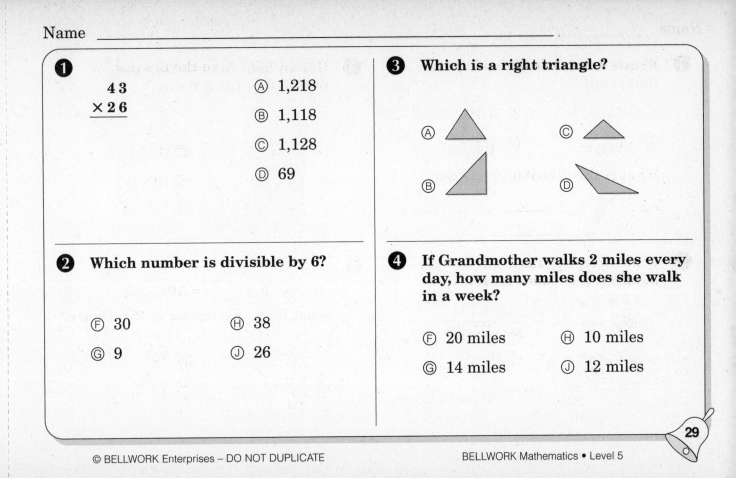

Ⓐ

Ⓒ

Ⓑ

Ⓓ

4 **If Grandmother walks 2 miles every day, how many miles does she walk in a week?**

Ⓕ 20 miles Ⓗ 10 miles

Ⓖ 14 miles Ⓙ 12 miles

29

Name _____

1 **Round 495,612 to the nearest ten thousand.**

Ⓐ 490,000   Ⓒ 400,000

Ⓑ 496,000   Ⓓ 500,000

2

```
  9 2 0
  4 5 5
+ 3 5 8
```

Ⓕ 1,734

Ⓖ 1,733

Ⓗ 1,743

Ⓙ 1,843

Ⓚ none of these

3 **Use an inch ruler to find the perimeter of this figure.**

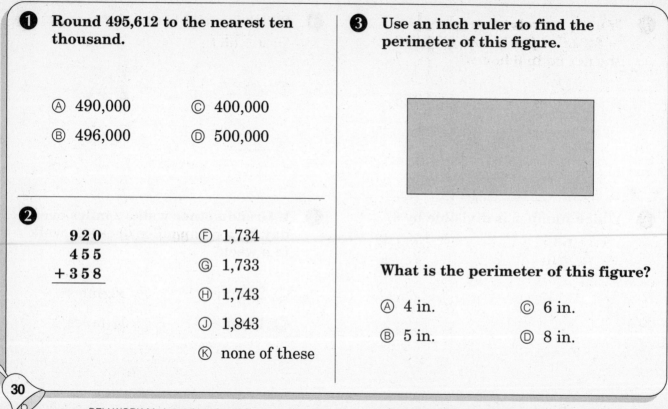

What is the perimeter of this figure?

Ⓐ 4 in.   Ⓒ 6 in.

Ⓑ 5 in.   Ⓓ 8 in.

Name _____

1 If a car travels at an average speed of 38 miles per hour, how far can the car go in 6 hours?

Ⓐ 6.3 miles　　Ⓒ 266 miles

Ⓑ 228 miles　　Ⓓ 44 miles

3

9)1,854

Ⓐ 260

Ⓑ 205 R1

Ⓒ 207

Ⓓ 206

2

$ 389.65
+ 437.20

Ⓕ $836.85

Ⓖ $826.85

Ⓗ $825.85

Ⓙ $826.95

4

900 + 60 + 4 =

Ⓕ 964　　Ⓗ 469

Ⓖ 946　　Ⓙ 694

31

1 The window was fifth from the bottom. How many windows were below it?

Ⓐ 5 windows   Ⓒ 4 windows

Ⓑ 2 windows   Ⓓ 0 windows

2 Find the median of the numbers 6, 10, 12, and 15.

Ⓕ 10   Ⓗ 11

Ⓖ 12   Ⓙ 11.5

3

$$800 + 40 + 9 =$$

Ⓐ 984   Ⓒ 894

Ⓑ 849   Ⓓ 489

4 Which sign belongs in the ◯ below?

$$\frac{1}{3} \bigcirc \frac{1}{4}$$

Ⓕ >   Ⓖ =   Ⓗ <

Name _____

❶

$$21 \div \boxed{} = 7$$

Ⓐ 4   Ⓒ 3

Ⓑ 5   Ⓓ 2

❷

$$\begin{array}{r} 4{,}339 \\ +\ 9{,}880 \\ \hline \end{array}$$

Ⓕ 14,210

Ⓖ 13,119

Ⓗ 14,219

Ⓙ 13,110

❸ **There are 24 cans of tuna in a case. How many cans are in 10 cases?**

Ⓐ 120 cans   Ⓒ 34 cans

Ⓑ 240 cans   Ⓓ 200 cans

❹ **A movie began at 2:05 p.m. and was over at 2:50 p.m. How many minutes long was the movie?**

Ⓕ 35 minutes   Ⓗ 45 minutes

Ⓖ 100 minutes   Ⓙ 65 minutes

33

❶

$$\begin{array}{r} 30 \\ \times\ 25 \\ \hline \end{array}$$

Ⓐ 55

Ⓑ 750

Ⓒ 650

Ⓓ 755

❸ **Running Wolf's grandfather is 78 years old. Running Wolf is 19 years old. How many years older than Running Wolf is his grandfather?**

Ⓐ 59 years   Ⓒ 97 years

Ⓑ 69 years   Ⓓ 58 years

❷

$$600 + 7 =$$

Ⓕ 670   Ⓗ 607

Ⓖ 760   Ⓙ 617

❹

$$\begin{array}{r} 6\frac{4}{5} \\ -\ 3\frac{1}{5} \\ \hline \end{array}$$

Ⓕ $3\frac{5}{5}$ Ⓗ 10

Ⓖ $3\frac{3}{5}$ Ⓙ $3\frac{2}{5}$

❶ 15 is divisible by which number?

Ⓐ 4   Ⓒ 6

Ⓑ 3   Ⓓ 7

---

❷

$$\begin{array}{r} 460 \\ -\ 218 \\ \hline \end{array}$$

Ⓕ 242

Ⓖ 678

Ⓗ 258

Ⓙ 252

Ⓚ none of these

❸ Anthony lived in the sixth house from the corner. How many houses were between the corner and Anthony's house?

Ⓐ 3 houses   Ⓒ 4 houses

Ⓑ 5 houses   Ⓓ 6 houses

---

❹

$$\begin{array}{r} 365 \\ \times\ \ \ 7 \\ \hline \end{array}$$

Ⓕ 2,155

Ⓖ 2,555

Ⓗ 2,545

Ⓙ 2,565

Ⓚ none of these

35

Name _____

1   **5 hr 30 min**
      + 4 hr 20 min

ⓐ 1 hr 10 min   ⓒ 9 hr 50 min

ⓑ 10 hr 40 min   ⓓ 8 hr 50 min

3 There are _____ feet in a yard.

ⓐ $\frac{1}{3}$ ⓒ 10

ⓑ 3   ⓓ 12

2
      $ 7.31
      − 5.19

ⓕ $12.50

ⓖ $2.12

ⓗ $2.28

ⓙ $2.22

4 Use the associative property to answer the problem below.

$$8 + (6 + 7) = (8 + 6) + \boxed{}$$

ⓕ 13   ⓗ 7

ⓖ 21   ⓙ 14

36

Name _____

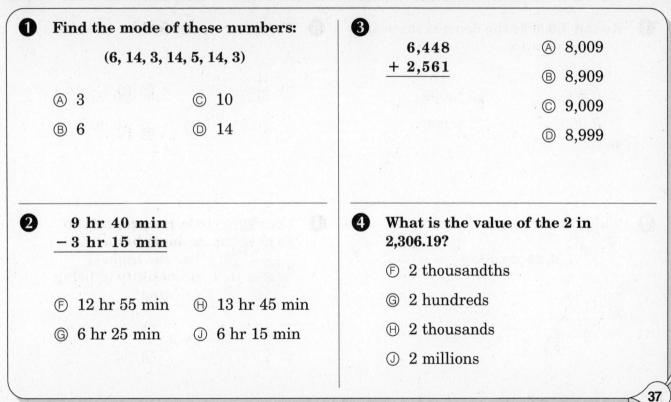

❶ Find the mode of these numbers:

(6, 14, 3, 14, 5, 14, 3)

Ⓐ 3   Ⓒ 10

Ⓑ 6   Ⓓ 14

❷   9 hr 40 min
      − 3 hr 15 min

Ⓕ 12 hr 55 min   Ⓗ 13 hr 45 min

Ⓖ 6 hr 25 min   Ⓙ 6 hr 15 min

❸

6,448
+ 2,561

Ⓐ 8,009

Ⓑ 8,909

Ⓒ 9,009

Ⓓ 8,999

❹ What is the value of the 2 in 2,306.19?

Ⓕ 2 thousandths

Ⓖ 2 hundreds

Ⓗ 2 thousands

Ⓙ 2 millions

37

Name _____

1 **Round 7,590 to the nearest thousand.**

Ⓐ 7,600 Ⓒ 8,000

Ⓑ 7,000 Ⓓ 9,000

3 **2 quarters + 3 dimes + 6 pennies =**

Ⓐ $0.76 Ⓒ $0.86

Ⓑ $0.61 Ⓓ $0.96

2 **What number comes next?**

6, 15, 24, 33, ____

Ⓕ 41 Ⓗ 43

Ⓖ 42 Ⓙ 44

4 **On one spin of the spinner, which letter has the highest probability of being selected?**

Ⓕ A Ⓗ C

Ⓖ B

❶

8,405
− 4,697

Ⓐ 13,102

Ⓑ 4,292

Ⓒ 3,708

Ⓓ 3,718

❸

$ 3.24
×   2

Ⓐ $6.48

Ⓑ $6.46

Ⓒ $6.58

Ⓓ $6.38

❷ **Which list has the numbers in order from greatest value to least value?**

Ⓕ $\frac{1}{4}$, $\frac{1}{3}$, $\frac{1}{2}$ Ⓗ $\frac{1}{2}$, $\frac{1}{4}$, $\frac{1}{3}$

Ⓖ $\frac{1}{3}$, $\frac{1}{4}$, $\frac{1}{2}$ Ⓙ $\frac{1}{2}$, $\frac{1}{3}$, $\frac{1}{4}$

❹ **Bill sold 170 ornaments in a school sale. Alyssa sold 143. How many more ornaments did Bill sell?**

Ⓕ 313 ornaments   Ⓗ 27 ornaments

Ⓖ 33 ornaments   Ⓙ 37 ornaments

39

Name _____

1 The standard numeral for the Roman numeral **XIII** is:

Ⓐ 8   Ⓒ 23

Ⓑ 13   Ⓓ 53

---

2 Three cars were driven to the picnic. There were four people in each car. How many people went to the picnic in the cars?

Ⓕ 9 people   Ⓗ 7 people

Ⓖ 10 people   Ⓙ 12 people

3

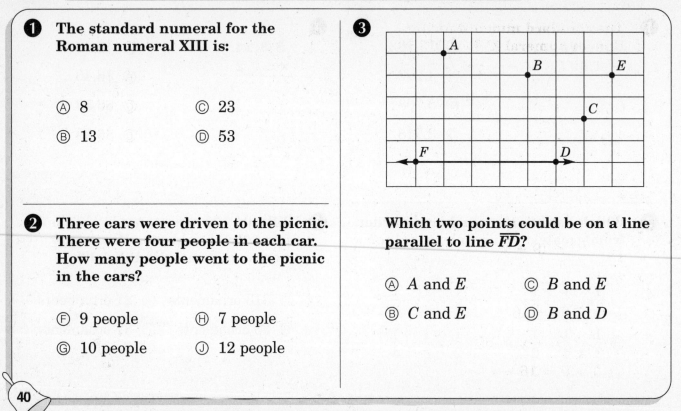

Which two points could be on a line parallel to line $\overline{FD}$?

Ⓐ A and E   Ⓒ B and E

Ⓑ C and E   Ⓓ B and D

❶ The standard numeral for the Roman numeral XVII is:

Ⓐ 13   Ⓒ 17

Ⓑ 15   Ⓓ 19

❷ Which equation is the same as:

$$3 + (9 + x) = 16$$

Ⓕ $3 + 9 = 16 + x$

Ⓖ $3 + 9x = 16$

Ⓗ $(3 + 9) + x = 16$

Ⓙ $3 + 9 = 16 \div x$

❸

$$\begin{array}{r} 1\,4 \\ \times\,4\,5 \\ \hline \end{array}$$

Ⓐ 126

Ⓑ 650

Ⓒ 630

Ⓓ 59

❹ 6 thousands
4 hundreds
5 tens
3 ones =

Ⓕ 6,534   Ⓗ 6,453

Ⓖ 6,345   Ⓙ 3,546

41

Name _____

1 Anna had 4 T-shirts. Mother bought her 3 more. How many T-shirts does Anna have now? Select the correct number sentence.

Ⓐ $4 - 3 = 1$ Ⓒ $4 \times 3 = 12$

Ⓑ $4 + 3 = 7$ Ⓓ $7 - 3 = 4$

2 Which figure is a hexagon?

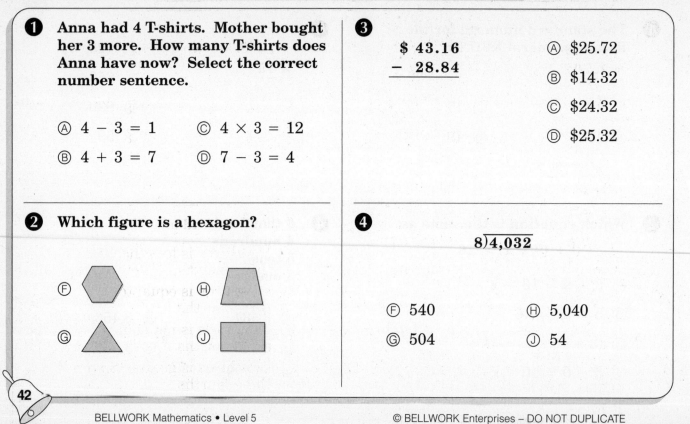

Ⓕ   Ⓗ

Ⓖ   Ⓙ

3
$$\begin{array}{r} \$\ 43.16 \\ -\ \ 28.84 \\ \hline \end{array}$$

Ⓐ $25.72

Ⓑ $14.32

Ⓒ $24.32

Ⓓ $25.32

4
$$8\overline{)4{,}032}$$

Ⓕ 540   Ⓗ 5,040

Ⓖ 504   Ⓙ 54

42

Name _____

❶

$$6{,}149 + 1{,}702$$

Ⓐ 7,841

Ⓑ 7,851

Ⓒ 7,951

Ⓓ 7,852

❷

$$\$\,3.56 \times 4$$

Ⓕ $14.04

Ⓖ $12.04

Ⓗ $12.24

Ⓙ $14.24

❸

$$8{,}000 + 40 + 9 =$$

Ⓐ 849

Ⓒ 8,049

Ⓑ 894

Ⓓ 8,940

❹ $\frac{2}{3} \,(<)\, \frac{3}{4}$ **is read as:**

Ⓕ two-thirds is less than three-fourths.

Ⓖ two-thirds is equal to three-fourths.

Ⓗ two-thirds is not equal to three-fourths.

Ⓙ two-thirds is greater than three-fourths.

43

Mr. Elm's class was asked to choose a favorite color. Each student picked only one favorite color. The graph below shows their choices.

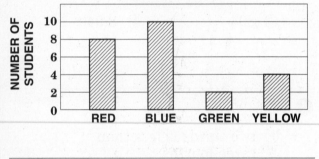

FAVORITE COLOR

1 **How many students chose green?**

Ⓐ 1 student   Ⓒ 4 students

Ⓑ 2 students   Ⓓ 5 students

2 **The color that ten students chose was —**

Ⓕ red.   Ⓗ blue.

Ⓖ green.   Ⓙ yellow.

3 **Which one of the following is a true statement about the graph on the left?**

Ⓐ More students chose green than yellow.

Ⓑ The number of students that chose either green or yellow equals the number of students that chose red.

Ⓒ Half as many students chose yellow as chose red.

Ⓓ The total number of students in the class was 26.

44

Name _____

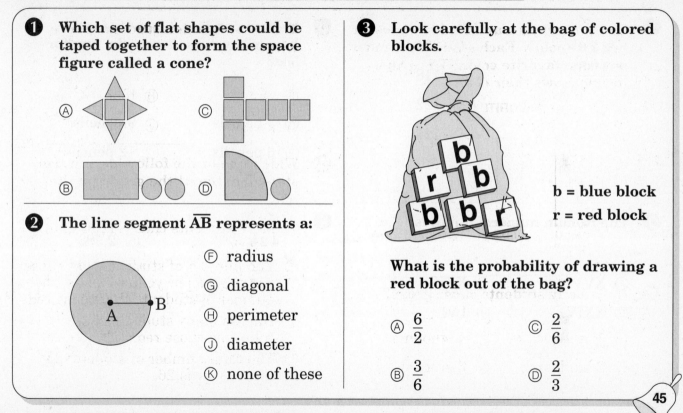

1 Which set of flat shapes could be taped together to form the space figure called a cone?

Ⓐ

Ⓒ

Ⓑ

Ⓓ

2 The line segment $\overline{AB}$ represents a:

Ⓕ radius

Ⓖ diagonal

Ⓗ perimeter

Ⓙ diameter

Ⓚ none of these

3 Look carefully at the bag of colored blocks.

b = blue block

r = red block

What is the probability of drawing a red block out of the bag?

Ⓐ $\dfrac{6}{2}$ Ⓒ $\dfrac{2}{6}$

Ⓑ $\dfrac{3}{6}$ Ⓓ $\dfrac{2}{3}$

45

1

$$\begin{array}{r} 2\,2\,6 \\ -\,1\,0\,8 \\ \hline \end{array}$$

Ⓐ 334

Ⓑ 118

Ⓒ 122

Ⓓ 128

3 **If Terri can buy 3 pencils for 25¢, how many pencils can she buy for 50¢?**

Ⓐ 3 pencils   Ⓒ 9 pencils

Ⓑ 6 pencils   Ⓓ 12 pencils

2 **The Roman numeral for 26 is:**

Ⓕ XVVI   Ⓗ XXVI

Ⓖ XXIV   Ⓙ LVI

4

$$\begin{array}{r} 4\,2\,6 \\ \times\quad 7 \\ \hline \end{array}$$

Ⓕ 2,992

Ⓖ 2,972

Ⓗ 2,982

Ⓙ 2,882

Name _____

❶

$$44 \times 22$$

Ⓐ 66

Ⓑ 968

Ⓒ 978

Ⓓ 176

❸ Which list has the numbers in order from least value to greatest value?

Ⓐ $\frac{1}{2}$, $\frac{2}{3}$, $\frac{3}{4}$ Ⓒ $\frac{3}{4}$, $\frac{1}{2}$, $\frac{2}{3}$

Ⓑ $\frac{3}{4}$, $\frac{2}{3}$, $\frac{1}{2}$ Ⓓ $\frac{1}{2}$, $\frac{3}{4}$, $\frac{2}{3}$

❷ The teacher's desk is 48 inches long. How many feet is 48 inches?

Ⓕ 4 feet   Ⓗ 3 feet

Ⓖ 8 feet   Ⓙ 6 feet

❹

$$280 - 135$$

Ⓕ 145

Ⓖ 155

Ⓗ 415

Ⓙ 150

47

Name _____

1 If Jason can wash 6 cars in 1 hour, how many cars can he wash in 3 hours?

Ⓐ 5 cars   Ⓒ 18 cars

Ⓑ 9 cars   Ⓓ 24 cars

2

$$\begin{array}{r} \$\ 6.23 \\ -\ 4.18 \\ \hline \end{array}$$

Ⓕ $10.41

Ⓖ $1.05

Ⓗ $2.15

Ⓙ $2.05

3 What is the value of the 6 in 60,543?

Ⓐ 6 thousands

Ⓑ 6 ten thousands

Ⓒ 6 hundred thousands

Ⓓ 6 millions

4 A guitar has six strings. Which equation below could be used to find "s," the number of strings needed for five guitars?

Ⓕ $6 \div 5 = s$ Ⓗ $s \times 5 = 6$

Ⓖ $6 + 5 = s$ Ⓙ $6 \times 5 = s$

Name _____

1 **Tracey and Tom played 5 sets of tennis. Tracey won only the fifth set. How many sets did Tom win?**

Ⓐ 4 sets   Ⓒ 5 sets

Ⓑ 6 sets   Ⓓ 3 sets

2

$$9,000 + 60 + 7 =$$

Ⓕ 9,607   Ⓗ 90,067

Ⓖ 967   Ⓙ 9,067

3

$$\begin{array}{r} \frac{2}{3} \\ - \frac{1}{3} \\ \hline \end{array}$$

Ⓐ 1   Ⓒ $\frac{3}{6}$

Ⓑ $\frac{1}{6}$ Ⓓ $\frac{1}{3}$

4

$$\begin{array}{r} 4\,4\,0 \\ -2\,0\,6 \\ \hline \end{array}$$

Ⓕ 246

Ⓖ 234

Ⓗ 240

Ⓙ 646

Ⓚ none of these

49

Name _____

1 Nghia kicked the football 45 yards. How many feet is 45 yards?

(A) 145 feet   (C) 15 feet

(B) 90 feet   (D) 135 feet

2 Use the associative property to answer the problem below.

$$5 + (\square + 3) = (5 + 7) + 3$$

(F) 10   (H) 7

(G) 12   (J) 15

3 What shape would come next in the pattern?

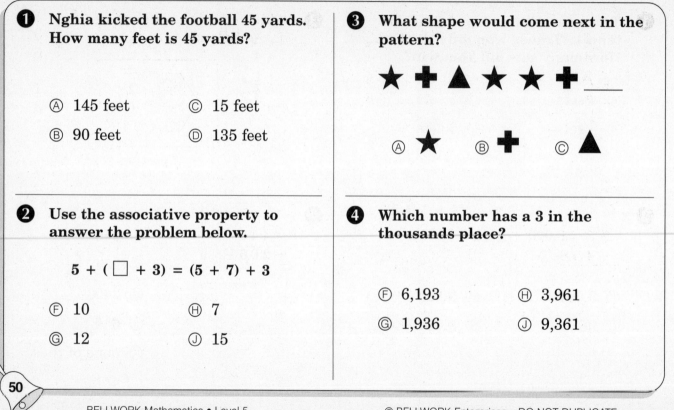

★ ✚ ▲ ★ ★ ✚ ____

(A) ★   (B) ✚   (C) ▲

4 Which number has a 3 in the thousands place?

(F) 6,193   (H) 3,961

(G) 1,936   (J) 9,361

50

Name _____

❶

$$\frac{1}{4}$$
$$+ \frac{2}{4}$$

Ⓐ $\frac{3}{4}$ Ⓒ $\frac{2}{4}$

Ⓑ $\frac{3}{5}$ Ⓓ $\frac{3}{8}$

❷

$$\begin{array}{r} \$\,8.42 \\ -\ 4.18 \\ \hline \end{array}$$

Ⓕ $12.60

Ⓖ $4.24

Ⓗ $3.36

Ⓙ $4.36

❸ **Which shows a reflection of the figure below?**

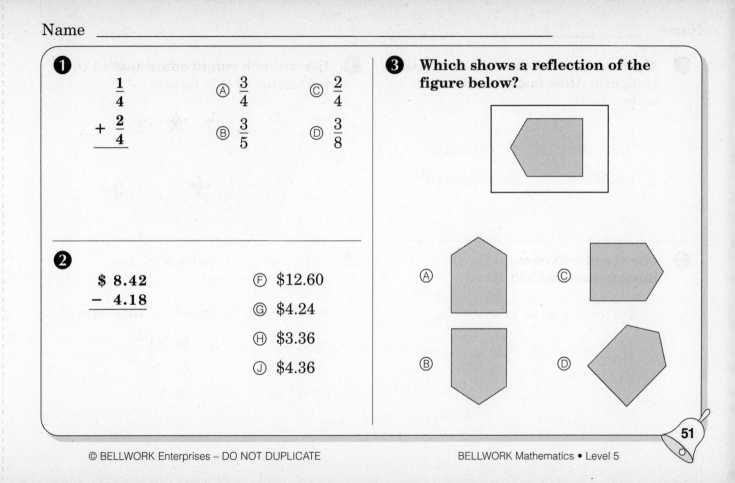

Ⓐ   Ⓒ

Ⓑ   Ⓓ

51

Name _____

1 There are ten children in line. Lisa is eighth. How many children are before her?

Ⓐ 9 children   Ⓒ 7 children

Ⓑ 6 children   Ⓓ 2 children

2 The standard numeral for the Roman numeral XVI is:

Ⓕ 14   Ⓗ 16

Ⓖ 91   Ⓙ 51

3 Use an inch ruler to find the perimeter of this figure.

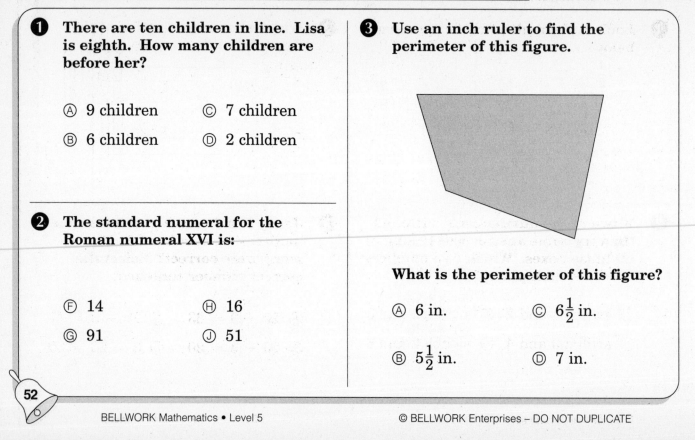

What is the perimeter of this figure?

Ⓐ 6 in.   Ⓒ $6\frac{1}{2}$ in.

Ⓑ $5\frac{1}{2}$ in.   Ⓓ 7 in.

Name _____

1 **Look at the multiplication problems below.**

$$1 \times 12 = \square$$

$$2 \times 4 = \square$$

$$3 \times 6 = \square$$

If two of the numbers are switched, then the same answer will belong in all three boxes. Which two numbers should switch places?

Ⓐ switch 1 and 2   Ⓒ switch 2 and 3

Ⓑ switch 3 and 4   Ⓓ switch 2 and 6

2
$$\begin{array}{r} 7\,0 \\ \times\ 4 \\ \hline \end{array}$$

Ⓕ 74

Ⓖ 240

Ⓗ 280

Ⓙ 284

3 **Jenny had 20 math problems on a math test. She missed 3. How many were correct? Select the correct number sentence.**

Ⓐ 20 + 3 = 23   Ⓒ 20 − 3 = 17

Ⓑ 23 − 3 = 20   Ⓓ 3 × 20 = 60

53

Name _____

❶ Which number is divisible by 4?

Ⓐ 34   Ⓒ 12

Ⓑ 46   Ⓓ 14

❷ Which of the drawings below shows oblique lines?

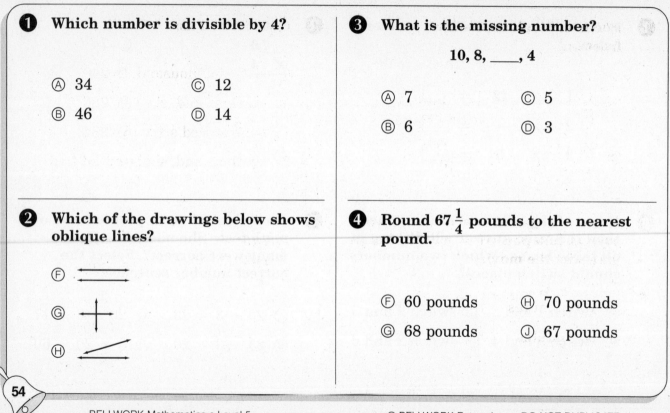

Ⓕ

Ⓖ

Ⓗ

❸ What is the missing number?

10, 8, ____, 4

Ⓐ 7   Ⓒ 5

Ⓑ 6   Ⓓ 3

❹ Round $67\frac{1}{4}$ pounds to the nearest pound.

Ⓕ 60 pounds   Ⓗ 70 pounds

Ⓖ 68 pounds   Ⓙ 67 pounds

Name _____

1 97% is equivalent to which fraction?

Ⓐ $\dfrac{97}{10}$ Ⓒ $\dfrac{97}{1000}$

Ⓑ $\dfrac{97}{1}$ Ⓓ $\dfrac{97}{100}$

2 A movie began at 1:05 p.m. and was over at 2:50 p.m. How many minutes long was the movie?

Ⓕ 150 minutes   Ⓗ 45 minutes

Ⓖ 65 minutes   Ⓙ 105 minutes

3 6,602 is read as:

Ⓐ sixty-six thousand, two

Ⓑ six thousand, sixty-two

Ⓒ six hundred sixty-two

Ⓓ six thousand, six hundred two

4

$$\begin{array}{r} 745 \\ +\ 165 \\ \hline \end{array}$$

Ⓕ 915

Ⓖ 620

Ⓗ 910

Ⓙ 580

55

Name _____

1 If there are 12 candy bars in 4 boxes, how many candy bars are in 8 boxes?

Ⓐ 36 bars   Ⓒ 24 bars

Ⓑ 8 bars   Ⓓ 16 bars

2
```
   3 hr  20 min
+ 5 hr  25 min
```

Ⓕ 8 hr 45 min   Ⓗ 2 hr 5 min

Ⓖ 9 hr 25 min   Ⓙ 9 hr 45 min

3 Which of the following figures is a sphere?

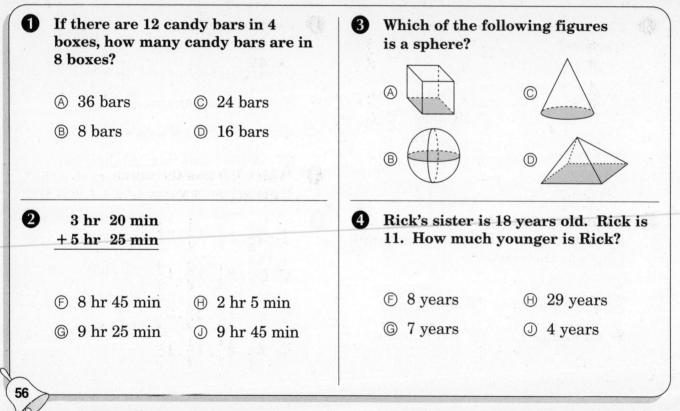

Ⓐ   Ⓒ

Ⓑ   Ⓓ

4 Rick's sister is 18 years old. Rick is 11. How much younger is Rick?

Ⓕ 8 years   Ⓗ 29 years

Ⓖ 7 years   Ⓙ 4 years

Name _____

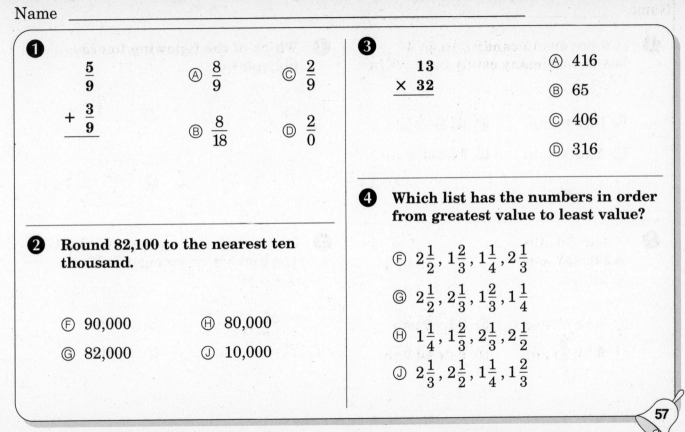

1

$$\frac{5}{9}$$
$$+ \frac{3}{9}$$

Ⓐ $\frac{8}{9}$ Ⓒ $\frac{2}{9}$

Ⓑ $\frac{8}{18}$ Ⓓ $\frac{2}{0}$

2 **Round 82,100 to the nearest ten thousand.**

Ⓕ 90,000 Ⓗ 80,000

Ⓖ 82,000 Ⓙ 10,000

3

$$\begin{array}{r} 13 \\ \times\ 32 \\ \hline \end{array}$$

Ⓐ 416

Ⓑ 65

Ⓒ 406

Ⓓ 316

4 **Which list has the numbers in order from greatest value to least value?**

Ⓕ $2\frac{1}{2}, 1\frac{2}{3}, 1\frac{1}{4}, 2\frac{1}{3}$

Ⓖ $2\frac{1}{2}, 2\frac{1}{3}, 1\frac{2}{3}, 1\frac{1}{4}$

Ⓗ $1\frac{1}{4}, 1\frac{2}{3}, 2\frac{1}{3}, 2\frac{1}{2}$

Ⓙ $2\frac{1}{3}, 2\frac{1}{2}, 1\frac{1}{4}, 1\frac{2}{3}$

57

1

$$\begin{array}{r} 6 \text{ hr} \quad 50 \text{ min} \\ -5 \text{ hr} \quad 15 \text{ min} \\ \hline \end{array}$$

Ⓐ 1 hr 25 min   Ⓒ 12 hr 5 min

Ⓑ 1 hr 35 min   Ⓓ 1 hr 45 min

2

$$\begin{array}{r} \$ \, 65.85 \\ + \, 29.06 \\ \hline \end{array}$$

Ⓕ $94.81

Ⓖ $94.91

Ⓗ $95.91

Ⓙ $85.81

3 **Which of the figures below is <u>not</u> a polygon?**

Ⓐ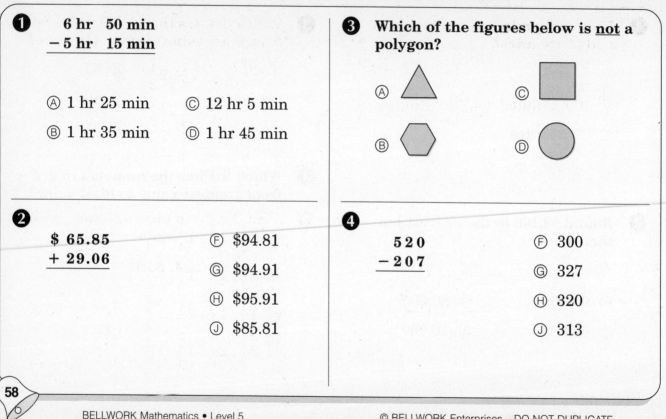

Ⓑ

Ⓒ

Ⓓ

4

$$\begin{array}{r} 520 \\ -207 \\ \hline \end{array}$$

Ⓕ 300

Ⓖ 327

Ⓗ 320

Ⓙ 313

58

Name _____

1 How many minutes are in 1 hour and 20 minutes?

(A) 120 minutes (C) 70 minutes

(B) 80 minutes (D) 60 minutes

2

$$\begin{array}{r} 3\,8\,0 \\ \times\ 2 \\ \hline \end{array}$$

(F) 660

(G) 762

(H) 670

(J) 780

(K) none of these

3 Which list has the numbers in order from least value to greatest value?

(A) $1\frac{1}{8}, 1\frac{2}{3}, 2\frac{1}{4}, 2\frac{1}{2}$

(B) $1\frac{2}{3}, 1\frac{1}{8}, 2\frac{1}{4}, 2\frac{1}{2}$

(C) $2\frac{1}{2}, 2\frac{1}{4}, 1\frac{2}{3}, 1\frac{1}{8}$

(D) $1\frac{1}{8}, 1\frac{2}{3}, 2\frac{1}{2}, 2\frac{1}{4}$

4 Find the mean (average) of the following numbers:

$$(2, 4, 6, 0)$$

(F) 4 (H) 2

(G) 3 (J) 12

❶

$$\begin{array}{r} 3\,0\,4 \\ \times\ \ 12 \\ \hline \end{array}$$

Ⓐ 3,638

Ⓑ 912

Ⓒ 4,648

Ⓓ 3,648

❷ Which number is divisible by 2 and 3?

Ⓕ 5

Ⓖ 9

Ⓗ 6

Ⓙ 8

❸ 6 apples are needed to make an apple pie. How many pies can be made from 18 apples?

Ⓐ 6 pies   Ⓒ 9 pies

Ⓑ 3 pies   Ⓓ 24 pies

❹

This angle is —

Ⓕ exactly 180°.

Ⓖ more than 90° and less than 180°.

Ⓗ more than 0° and less than 90°.

Ⓙ an acute angle.

1 There are 7 baseball teams in the league. There are 9 players on each team. How many players are in the league? Select the correct number sentence.

Ⓐ $9 - 7 = 2$ Ⓒ $9 + 7 = 16$

Ⓑ $7 \times 9 = 63$ Ⓓ $7 + 9 = 16$

2

$$237 + 16 =$$

Ⓕ 243   Ⓗ 253

Ⓖ 263   Ⓙ 397

3

$$\frac{3}{4}$$
$$- \frac{2}{4}$$

Ⓐ $\frac{5}{4}$ Ⓒ $\frac{1}{4}$

Ⓑ $\frac{2}{4}$ Ⓓ $\frac{1}{8}$

4 Use the commutative property to answer the problem below.

$$\square + 8 = 8 + 7$$

Ⓕ 15   Ⓗ 16

Ⓖ 7   Ⓙ 8

Name _____

1

$$4\,10$$
$$\times\ 20$$

Ⓐ 9,200

Ⓑ 8,200

Ⓒ 920

Ⓓ 820

3

$$\$\ 72.28$$
$$+\ 19.06$$

Ⓐ $91.24

Ⓑ $81.34

Ⓒ $91.34

Ⓓ $63.22

2 Today is Wednesday. Tomorrow is Ted's birthday. On what day is Ted's birthday?

Ⓕ Tuesday   Ⓗ Sunday

Ⓖ Friday   Ⓙ Thursday

4 The Roman numeral for 110 is:

Ⓕ LX   Ⓗ MX

Ⓖ CX   Ⓙ DX

Name _____

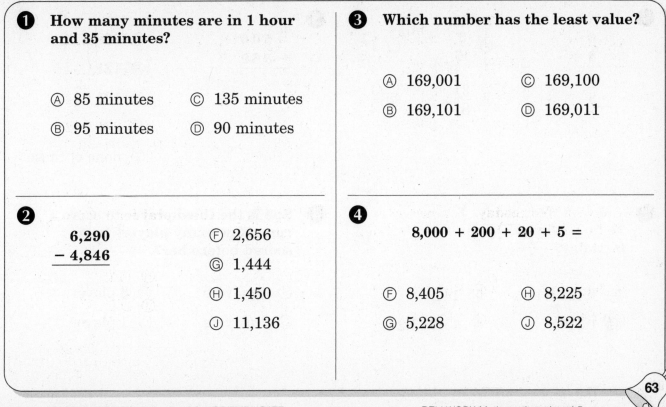

1 How many minutes are in 1 hour and 35 minutes?

Ⓐ 85 minutes   Ⓒ 135 minutes

Ⓑ 95 minutes   Ⓓ 90 minutes

2

6,290
− 4,846

Ⓕ 2,656

Ⓖ 1,444

Ⓗ 1,450

Ⓙ 11,136

3 Which number has the least value?

Ⓐ 169,001   Ⓒ 169,100

Ⓑ 169,101   Ⓓ 169,011

4

$$8,000 + 200 + 20 + 5 =$$

Ⓕ 8,405   Ⓗ 8,225

Ⓖ 5,228   Ⓙ 8,522

63

1

$$\frac{6}{8}$$
$$-\frac{3}{8}$$

(A) $\frac{3}{16}$

(B) $\frac{3}{8}$

(C) $1\frac{1}{8}$

(D) $\frac{1}{4}$

3

$$\begin{array}{r} 5\,0\,0 \\ -3\,6\,9 \end{array}$$

(A) 269

(B) 121

(C) 131

(D) 231

(E) none of these

2

$$5\,\overline{)\,7{,}006}$$

(F) 1,401 R1

(H) 141

(G) 1,410

(J) 1,401 R2

4 Sue is the third player to score a run. How many players have scored before her?

(F) 4 players

(H) 3 players

(G) 2 players

(J) 1 player

64

Name _____

1 Carly, Debi, Maya, and Joy each ran one lap around the track. Carly was 10 seconds faster than Debi. Maya was 5 seconds slower than Joy. Debi was 5 seconds faster than Joy. Which one of the following statements is true about how their times compared?

Ⓐ Debi was the fastest.
Ⓑ Debi and Joy had the same time.
Ⓒ Joy was third fastest.
Ⓓ Carly was second fastest.

2

$$\square \div 8 = 2$$

Ⓕ 4　　　　Ⓗ 16
Ⓖ 10　　　　Ⓙ 6

3

$$\begin{array}{r} \$\ 25.68 \\ -\ 14.99 \\ \hline \end{array}$$

Ⓐ $10.69
Ⓑ $10.79
Ⓒ $11.31
Ⓓ $10.68

4 What is the estimated answer?

$$83 + 69 + 31 = \square$$

Ⓕ 180　　　　Ⓗ 190
Ⓖ 170　　　　Ⓙ 160

65

The Venn diagram below shows two sports that 17 students play.

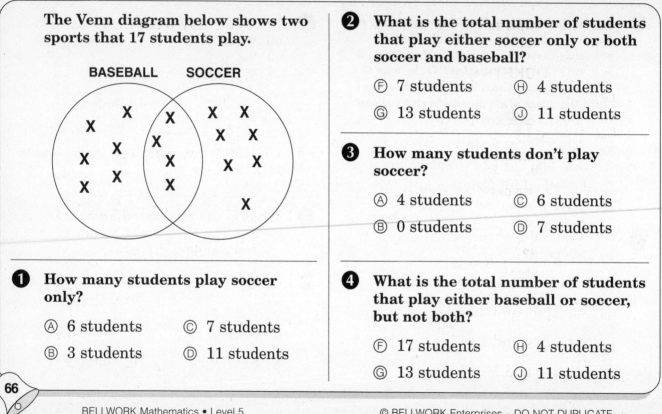

BASEBALL   SOCCER

❶ How many students play soccer only?

Ⓐ 6 students   Ⓒ 7 students

Ⓑ 3 students   Ⓓ 11 students

❷ What is the total number of students that play either soccer only or both soccer and baseball?

Ⓕ 7 students   Ⓗ 4 students

Ⓖ 13 students   Ⓙ 11 students

❸ How many students don't play soccer?

Ⓐ 4 students   Ⓒ 6 students

Ⓑ 0 students   Ⓓ 7 students

❹ What is the total number of students that play either baseball or soccer, but not both?

Ⓕ 17 students   Ⓗ 4 students

Ⓖ 13 students   Ⓙ 11 students

Use this graph to answer the next four questions.

TICKETS SOLD

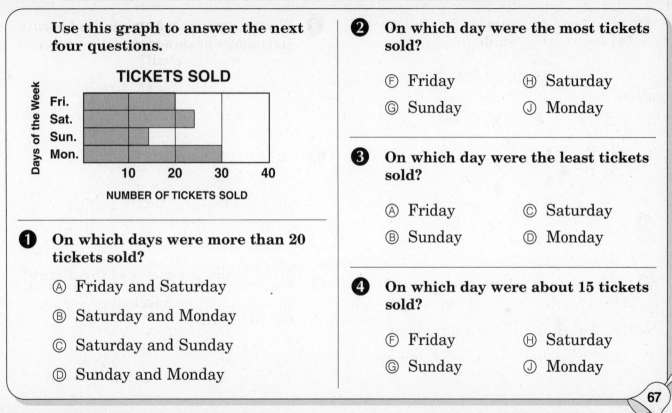

Days of the Week

Fri.
Sat.
Sun.
Mon.

10   20   30   40

NUMBER OF TICKETS SOLD

❶ **On which days were more than 20 tickets sold?**

Ⓐ Friday and Saturday

Ⓑ Saturday and Monday

Ⓒ Saturday and Sunday

Ⓓ Sunday and Monday

❷ **On which day were the most tickets sold?**

Ⓕ Friday   Ⓗ Saturday

Ⓖ Sunday   Ⓙ Monday

❸ **On which day were the least tickets sold?**

Ⓐ Friday   Ⓒ Saturday

Ⓑ Sunday   Ⓓ Monday

❹ **On which day were about 15 tickets sold?**

Ⓕ Friday   Ⓗ Saturday

Ⓖ Sunday   Ⓙ Monday

Name _____

1

$$\square \div 3 = 8$$

Ⓐ 11   Ⓒ 26

Ⓑ 5   Ⓓ 24

2

$$9 \times 5 = \boxed{}$$

Ⓕ 37 + 8   Ⓗ 95 ÷ 5

Ⓖ 42 + 4   Ⓙ 47 ÷ 5

3 **Use a centimeter ruler to find the perimeter of this figure.**

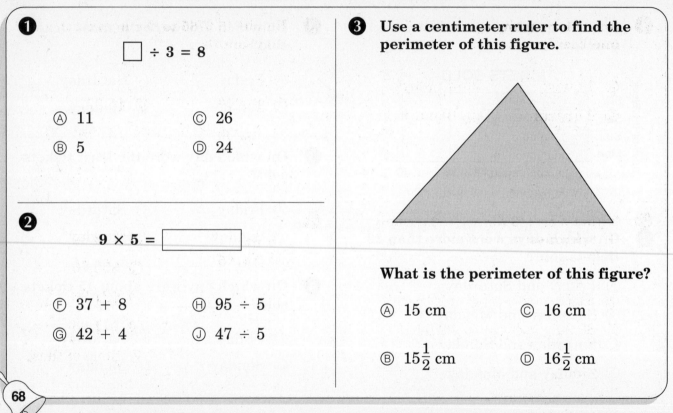

What is the perimeter of this figure?

Ⓐ 15 cm   Ⓒ 16 cm

Ⓑ $15\frac{1}{2}$ cm   Ⓓ $16\frac{1}{2}$ cm

Name _____

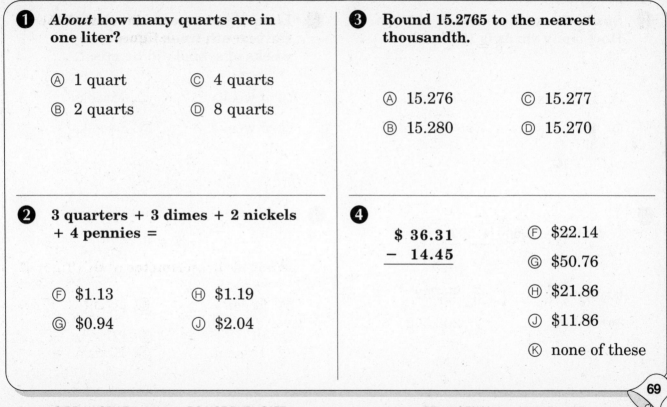

① ***About* how many quarts are in one liter?**

Ⓐ 1 quart   Ⓒ 4 quarts

Ⓑ 2 quarts   Ⓓ 8 quarts

② **3 quarters + 3 dimes + 2 nickels + 4 pennies =**

Ⓕ $1.13   Ⓗ $1.19

Ⓖ $0.94   Ⓙ $2.04

③ **Round 15.2765 to the nearest thousandth.**

Ⓐ 15.276   Ⓒ 15.277

Ⓑ 15.280   Ⓓ 15.270

④

$ 36.31
− 14.45

Ⓕ $22.14

Ⓖ $50.76

Ⓗ $21.86

Ⓙ $11.86

Ⓚ none of these

Name _____

1 Susan threw the baseball 135 feet. How many yards is 135 feet?

Ⓐ 13 yards   Ⓒ 35 yards

Ⓑ 45 yards   Ⓓ 405 yards

2

$$20{,}000 + 6{,}000 + 500 + 2 =$$

Ⓕ 20,652   Ⓗ 26,052

Ⓖ 26,502   Ⓙ 206,502

3 Liam did not start school until the seventh week. How many weeks of school did he miss?

Ⓐ 4 weeks   Ⓒ 6 weeks

Ⓑ 5 weeks   Ⓓ 8 weeks

4

$$\Box \div 7 = 6$$

Ⓕ 13   Ⓗ 1

Ⓖ 48   Ⓙ 42

Name _____

1 **It is almost noon.**
What time is shown?

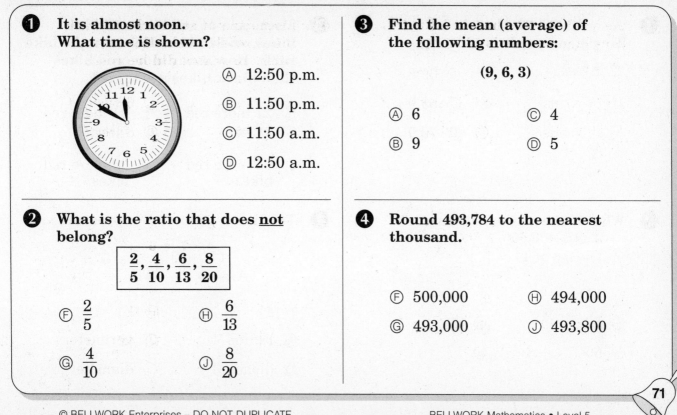

- Ⓐ 12:50 p.m.
- Ⓑ 11:50 p.m.
- Ⓒ 11:50 a.m.
- Ⓓ 12:50 a.m.

2 **What is the ratio that does <u>not</u> belong?**

$$\frac{2}{5}, \frac{4}{10}, \frac{6}{13}, \frac{8}{20}$$

- Ⓕ $\frac{2}{5}$
- Ⓗ $\frac{6}{13}$
- Ⓖ $\frac{4}{10}$
- Ⓙ $\frac{8}{20}$

3 **Find the mean (average) of the following numbers:**

(9, 6, 3)

- Ⓐ 6
- Ⓒ 4
- Ⓑ 9
- Ⓓ 5

4 **Round 493,784 to the nearest thousand.**

- Ⓕ 500,000
- Ⓗ 494,000
- Ⓖ 493,000
- Ⓙ 493,800

Name _____

❶

$$\begin{array}{r} 2\,3\,.3 \\ +\ 4\,6\,.5 \end{array}$$

- Ⓐ 70.8
- Ⓑ 69.8
- Ⓒ 69.9
- Ⓓ 70.9

❷ **What is the estimated answer?**

$$6 \times 11 = \boxed{}$$

- Ⓕ 50
- Ⓗ 80
- Ⓖ 60
- Ⓙ 17

❸ There are 44 red bikes, 23 blue bikes, and 17 black bikes in the bike rack. How many more red bikes than black bikes are there?

- Ⓐ 27 more red bikes
- Ⓒ 21 more red bikes
- Ⓑ 84 more red bikes
- Ⓓ 33 more red bikes

❹ The line segment $\overline{\text{AB}}$ represents a:

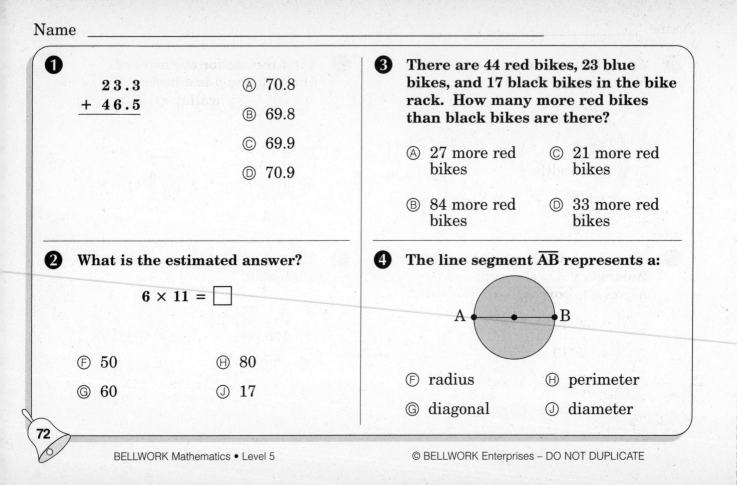

- Ⓕ radius
- Ⓗ perimeter
- Ⓖ diagonal
- Ⓙ diameter

1 **What is the value of the 8 in 30.86?**

Ⓐ 8 tens

Ⓑ 8 ones

Ⓒ 8 hundredths

Ⓓ 8 tenths

2 **Mary bought 3 books for $2.40 each. How much did the books cost? Select the correct number sentence.**

Ⓕ 3 × $2.40 = $7.20

Ⓖ 3 + $2.40 = $5.40

Ⓗ $2.40 ÷ 3 = $0.80

Ⓙ 3 − $2.40 = $0.60

3 **The formula for the area of a parallelogram is $A = bh$. What is the area of the parallelogram below?**

Ⓐ 14 cm²

Ⓑ 28 cm²

Ⓒ 60 cm²

Ⓓ 40 cm²

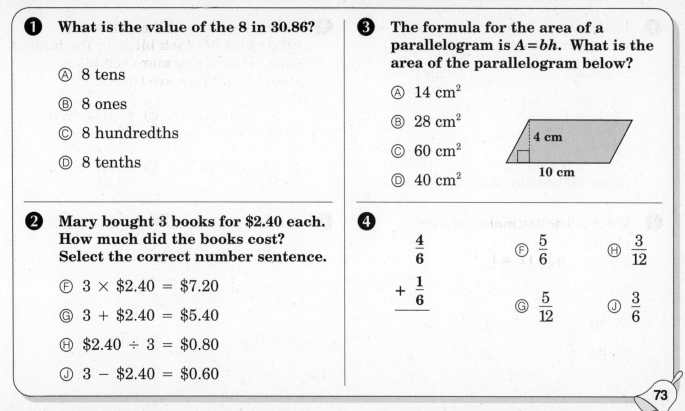

4 cm

10 cm

4

$$\frac{4}{6}$$
$$+ \frac{1}{6}$$

Ⓕ $\frac{5}{6}$

Ⓖ $\frac{5}{12}$

Ⓗ $\frac{3}{12}$

Ⓙ $\frac{3}{6}$

73

1 In the figure below, is the dotted line a line of symmetry?

Ⓐ yes   Ⓑ no

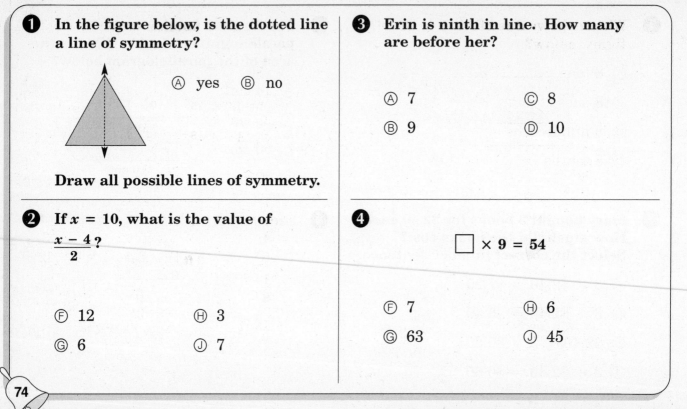

Draw all possible lines of symmetry.

2 If $x = 10$, what is the value of $\dfrac{x - 4}{2}$?

Ⓕ 12   Ⓗ 3

Ⓖ 6   Ⓙ 7

3 Erin is ninth in line. How many are before her?

Ⓐ 7   Ⓒ 8

Ⓑ 9   Ⓓ 10

4

$$\square \times 9 = 54$$

Ⓕ 7   Ⓗ 6

Ⓖ 63   Ⓙ 45

Name _____

1 **Which shows a reflection of the figure below?**

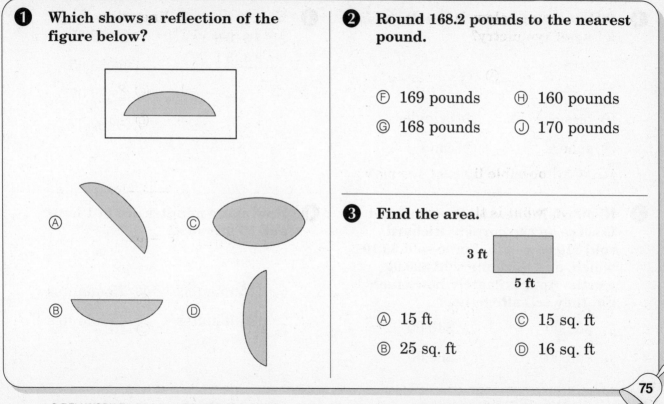

Ⓐ

Ⓒ

Ⓑ

Ⓓ

2 **Round 168.2 pounds to the nearest pound.**

Ⓕ 169 pounds   Ⓗ 160 pounds

Ⓖ 168 pounds   Ⓙ 170 pounds

3 **Find the area.**

3 ft

5 ft

Ⓐ 15 ft   Ⓒ 15 sq. ft

Ⓑ 25 sq. ft   Ⓓ 16 sq. ft

❶ **What is the name of this solid shape?**

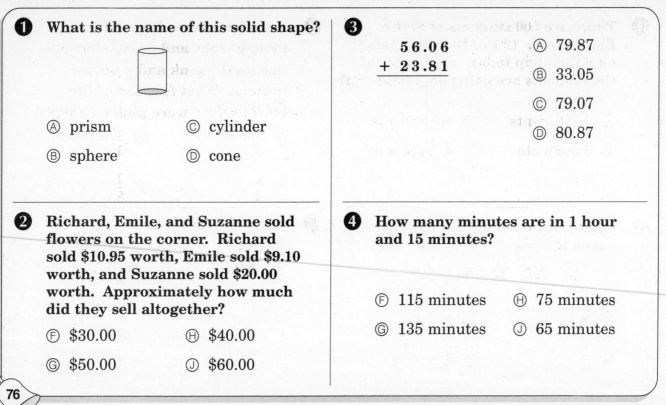

Ⓐ prism   Ⓒ cylinder

Ⓑ sphere   Ⓓ cone

❷ **Richard, Emile, and Suzanne sold flowers on the corner. Richard sold $10.95 worth, Emile sold $9.10 worth, and Suzanne sold $20.00 worth. Approximately how much did they sell altogether?**

Ⓕ $30.00   Ⓗ $40.00

Ⓖ $50.00   Ⓙ $60.00

❸

$$\begin{array}{r} 56.06 \\ + \ 23.81 \end{array}$$

Ⓐ 79.87

Ⓑ 33.05

Ⓒ 79.07

Ⓓ 80.87

❹ **How many minutes are in 1 hour and 15 minutes?**

Ⓕ 115 minutes   Ⓗ 75 minutes

Ⓖ 135 minutes   Ⓙ 65 minutes

Name _____

1 There are 500 students at Smith Elementary. 12% of them are going on a field trip today. How many of the students are going on a field trip?

Ⓐ 42 students   Ⓒ 60 students

Ⓑ 6 students   Ⓓ 41 students

2 What fraction of all the stars is shaded?

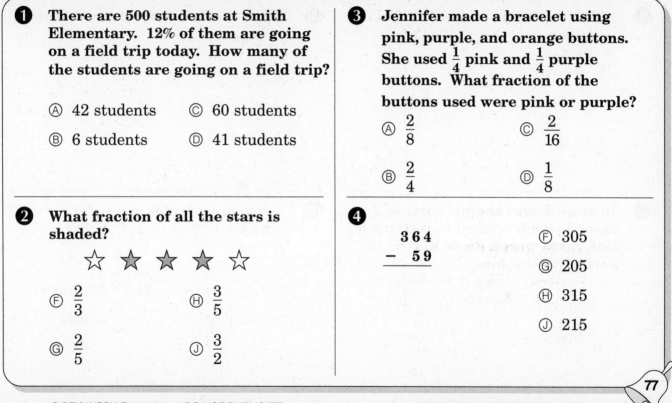

Ⓕ $\frac{2}{3}$ Ⓗ $\frac{3}{5}$

Ⓖ $\frac{2}{5}$ Ⓙ $\frac{3}{2}$

3 Jennifer made a bracelet using pink, purple, and orange buttons. She used $\frac{1}{4}$ pink and $\frac{1}{4}$ purple buttons. What fraction of the buttons used were pink or purple?

Ⓐ $\frac{2}{8}$ Ⓒ $\frac{2}{16}$

Ⓑ $\frac{2}{4}$ Ⓓ $\frac{1}{8}$

4

$$\begin{array}{r} 3\,6\,4 \\ -\ \ 5\,9 \\ \hline \end{array}$$

Ⓕ 305

Ⓖ 205

Ⓗ 315

Ⓙ 215

BELLWORK Mathematics • Level 5

Name _____

1

$$29.6$$
$$- \ 13.5$$

Ⓐ 43.1

Ⓑ 16.1

Ⓒ 6.1

Ⓓ 15.1

3 Which number sentence goes with
$27 \times 14 = \square$?

Ⓐ $\square - 14 = 27$

Ⓑ $27 + 14 = \square$

Ⓒ $27 \div 14 = \square$

Ⓓ $\square \div 14 = 27$

2 18 people came to your party in 3
cars. 9 people walked to your party.
How many people came to your
party?

Ⓕ 27 people   Ⓗ 30 people

Ⓖ 63 people   Ⓙ 18 people

4

$$382$$
$$\times \ \ 51$$

Ⓕ 2,292

Ⓖ 19,482

Ⓗ 19,382

Ⓙ 18,482

78

Name _____

❶ Which number is divisible by 2 and 4?

Ⓐ 6 Ⓒ 10

Ⓑ 8 Ⓓ 14

❸

$$20.04 \times 0.2$$

Ⓐ 4,008

Ⓑ 4.008

Ⓒ 40.08

Ⓓ 0.4008

❷ Round 612,496,582 to the nearest million.

Ⓕ 612,500,000 Ⓗ 613,000,000

Ⓖ 612,000,000 Ⓙ 600,000,000

❹ Which number has the greatest value?

Ⓕ 2.00 Ⓗ 2.07

Ⓖ 2.16 Ⓙ 2.20

BELLWORK Mathematics • Level 5

Name _____

1 **Round 379,461 to the nearest hundred thousand.**

Ⓐ 300,000   Ⓒ 380,000

Ⓑ 400,000   Ⓓ 379,500

2

$$6\overline{)1,547}$$

Ⓕ 258 R5   Ⓗ 257

Ⓖ 2,057   Ⓙ 257 R5

3 **Round $46.39 to the nearest dollar.**

Ⓐ $46.00   Ⓒ $45.00

Ⓑ $47.00   Ⓓ $46.40

4 **Which fraction has the least value?**

Ⓕ $\frac{1}{2}$ Ⓗ $\frac{1}{4}$

Ⓖ $\frac{1}{3}$ Ⓙ $\frac{1}{5}$

Name _____

1 **Use the associative property to answer the problem below.**

$$3 \times (2 \times 5) = (3 \times \boxed{}) \times 5$$

Ⓐ 10   Ⓒ 2

Ⓑ 7   Ⓓ 5

2

6 ft 5 in.
+ 3 ft 5 in.

Ⓕ 10 ft 10 in.

Ⓖ 10 ft

Ⓗ 9 ft 10 in.

Ⓙ 3 ft

3 **What shape would come next in the pattern?**

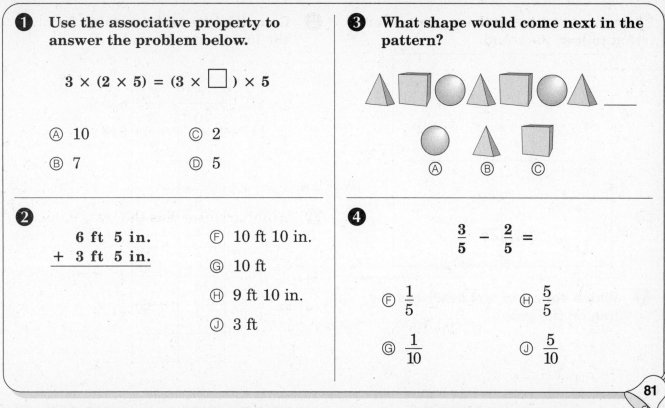

Ⓐ   Ⓑ   Ⓒ

4

$$\frac{3}{5} - \frac{2}{5} =$$

Ⓕ $\frac{1}{5}$ Ⓗ $\frac{5}{5}$

Ⓖ $\frac{1}{10}$ Ⓙ $\frac{5}{10}$

Use the graph to answer the questions that follow.

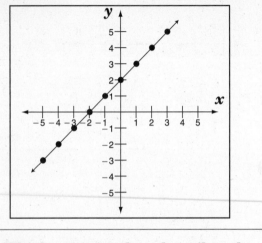

❶ Which equation *best* describes the line on the graph?

Ⓐ $y = x$ Ⓒ $y = 2x$

Ⓑ $y = x + 2$ Ⓓ $y = -x$

❷ Complete the function table for the line on the graph.

x	y
0	2
1	3
2	
3	
-1	
-2	
-3	
-4	
-5	

❶ Round to the nearest hundred million.

$$372{,}491{,}607$$

ⓐ 400,000,000   © 370,000,000

ⓑ 300,000,000   ⓓ 372,000,000

❷ The formula for the area of a rectangle is: *Area = length × width.* If two equal triangles can fit inside a rectangle, what is the formula for the area of a triangle?

ⓕ $A = l \times w$ Ⓗ $A = \dfrac{l \times w}{2}$

Ⓖ $A = 2(l \times w)$ ⓙ $A = (l \times w) + 2$

❸ Which point on the number line represents $2\frac{3}{4}$?

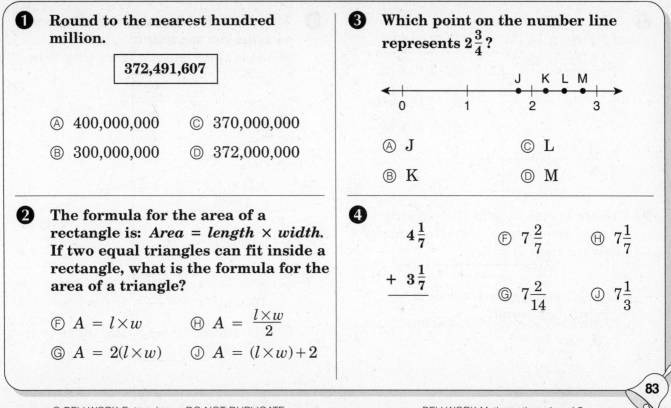

ⓐ J   © L

ⓑ K   ⓓ M

❹

$$\begin{aligned} 4\tfrac{1}{7} \\ + \ 3\tfrac{1}{7} \\ \hline \end{aligned}$$

ⓕ $7\frac{2}{7}$ Ⓗ $7\frac{1}{7}$

Ⓖ $7\frac{2}{14}$ ⓙ $7\frac{1}{3}$

83

1

4 ft 3 in.
+ 3 ft 8 in.

Ⓐ 6 ft 11 in.

Ⓑ 1 ft 5 in.

Ⓒ 7 ft 11 in.

Ⓓ 8 ft 1 in.

2 There are 48 cars in the parking lot. 8 cars are in each row. How many rows of cars are there?

Ⓕ 56 rows   Ⓗ 6 rows

Ⓖ 384 rows   Ⓙ 40 rows

3 Use an inch ruler and this diagram to help you answer the question. What is the distance from City A to City B?

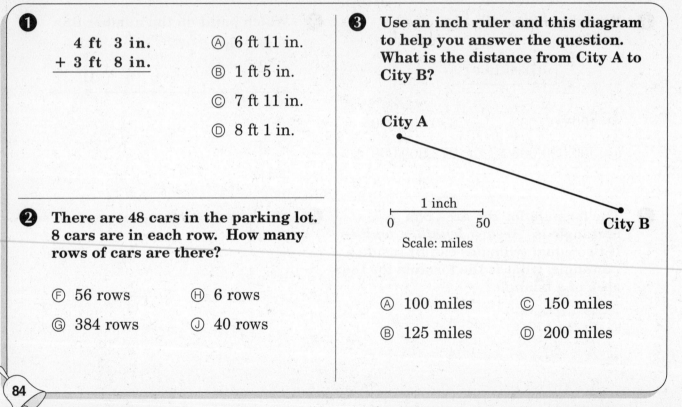

City A

1 inch

0   50

Scale: miles

City B

Ⓐ 100 miles   Ⓒ 150 miles

Ⓑ 125 miles   Ⓓ 200 miles

Name _____

1 The formula for the area of a parallelogram is $A = bh$. What is the area of the parallelogram below?

Ⓐ 72 m²

Ⓑ 36 m²

Ⓒ 18 m²

Ⓓ 96 m²

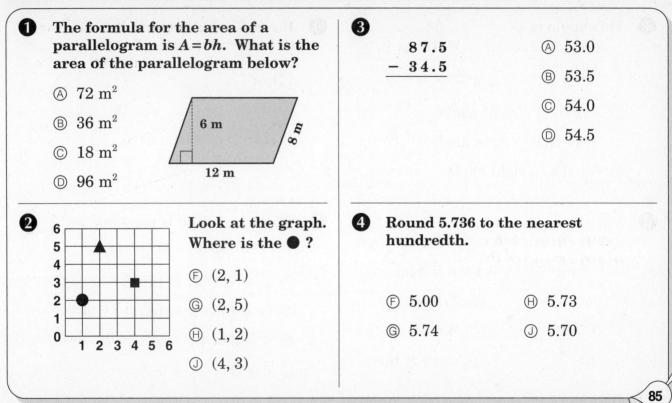

6 m

8 m

12 m

2

Look at the graph. Where is the ● ?

Ⓕ (2, 1)

Ⓖ (2, 5)

Ⓗ (1, 2)

Ⓙ (4, 3)

3

$$\begin{array}{r} 87.5 \\ -\ 34.5 \\ \hline \end{array}$$

Ⓐ 53.0

Ⓑ 53.5

Ⓒ 54.0

Ⓓ 54.5

4 Round 5.736 to the nearest hundredth.

Ⓕ 5.00

Ⓖ 5.74

Ⓗ 5.73

Ⓙ 5.70

85

Name _____

1 This angle is —

Ⓐ less than a right angle.

Ⓑ more than a right angle.

Ⓒ equal to a right angle.

2

$$2 \text{ ft } 6 \text{ in.}$$
$$+ 4 \text{ ft } 8 \text{ in.}$$

Ⓕ 7 ft 2 in.

Ⓖ 6 ft 4 in.

Ⓗ 7 ft 4 in.

Ⓙ 6 ft 10 in.

Ⓚ none of these

3 If $y = 5$, what is the value of $(5 \times y) - 4$?

Ⓐ 29   Ⓒ 14

Ⓑ 21   Ⓓ 6

4 Which equation is the same as:

$$x + (6 + 3) = 14$$

Ⓕ $x - (6 + 3) = 14$

Ⓖ $(x + 6) + 3 = 14$

Ⓗ $6 + 3 = 14 \div x$

Ⓙ $6 + 3 = 14 + x$

Name _____

1 **Which number is divisible by 2 and 5?**

Ⓐ 8   Ⓒ 10

Ⓑ 12   Ⓓ 15

2 **What is the missing number?**

7, 14, ___, 28

Ⓕ 20   Ⓗ 22

Ⓖ 21   Ⓙ 18

3 **The standard numeral for the Roman numeral LXV is:**

Ⓐ 115   Ⓒ 515

Ⓑ 65   Ⓓ 55

4

$$\begin{array}{r} 306 \\ \times\ 32 \end{array}$$

Ⓕ 9,792

Ⓖ 9,782

Ⓗ 1,530

Ⓙ 9,892

87

Name _____

1 Which is the *best* estimate for the measure of angle *B*?

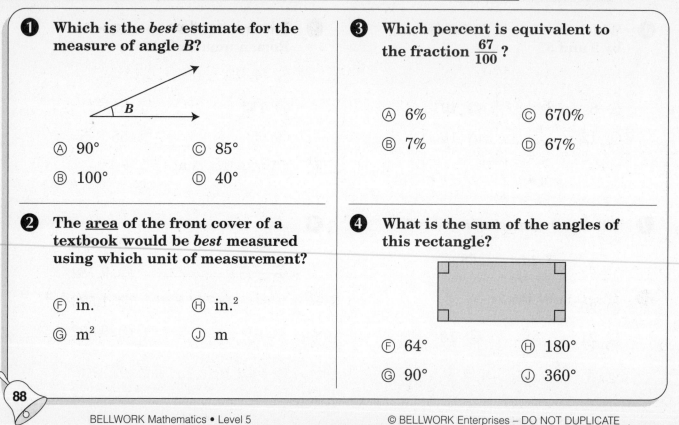

- (A) 90°
- (B) 100°
- (C) 85°
- (D) 40°

2 The <u>area</u> of the front cover of a textbook would be *best* measured using which unit of measurement?

- (F) in.
- (G) m²
- (H) in.²
- (J) m

3 Which percent is equivalent to the fraction $\frac{67}{100}$?

- (A) 6%
- (B) 7%
- (C) 670%
- (D) 67%

4 What is the sum of the angles of this rectangle?

- (F) 64°
- (G) 90°
- (H) 180°
- (J) 360°

88

Name _____

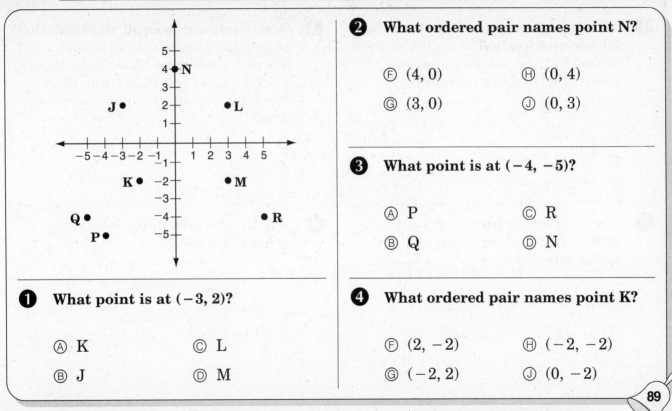

2 **What ordered pair names point N?**

Ⓕ (4, 0)   Ⓗ (0, 4)

Ⓖ (3, 0)   Ⓙ (0, 3)

3 **What point is at (−4, −5)?**

Ⓐ P   Ⓒ R

Ⓑ Q   Ⓓ N

1 **What point is at (−3, 2)?**

Ⓐ K   Ⓒ L

Ⓑ J   Ⓓ M

4 **What ordered pair names point K?**

Ⓕ (2, −2)   Ⓗ (−2, −2)

Ⓖ (−2, 2)   Ⓙ (0, −2)

Name _____

❶ An egg carton can hold a dozen eggs. Which equation below could be used to find "*e*," the number of eggs needed to fill 6 egg cartons?

Ⓐ $12 \div 6 = e$

Ⓑ $12 \times 6 = e$

Ⓒ $12 + 6 = e$

Ⓓ $12 \times e = 6$

---

❷

$$\begin{array}{r} \$\,91.42 \\ -\quad 8.39 \\ \hline \end{array}$$

Ⓕ $97.17

Ⓖ $97.27

Ⓗ $83.13

Ⓙ $83.03

Ⓚ none of these

---

❸ Greg, Sam, and Juan all played on the same soccer team last year. Sam scored 5 goals more than Greg. Juan scored 2 goals less than Sam. How many more goals did Juan score than Greg?

Ⓐ 5 goals   Ⓒ 7 goals

Ⓑ 2 goals   Ⓓ 3 goals

---

❹

$$\begin{array}{r} 8 \text{ hr } 33 \text{ min} \\ -5 \text{ hr } 28 \text{ min} \\ \hline \end{array}$$

Ⓕ 3 hr 5 min   Ⓗ 3 hr 15 min

Ⓖ 13 hr 63 min   Ⓙ 2 hr 15 min

90

Name _____

1 A plant grew 15 inches in 5 weeks. On the average, how many inches did it grow in a week?

Ⓐ 3 inches   Ⓒ 5 inches

Ⓑ 75 inches   Ⓓ 20 inches

3

$$3\frac{4}{6}$$
$$+\ 1\frac{1}{6}$$

Ⓐ $4\frac{5}{6}$ Ⓒ 5

Ⓑ $4\frac{5}{12}$ Ⓓ $2\frac{1}{2}$

2

```
    3 6
    5 2 9
 +   8 6
```

Ⓕ 651

Ⓖ 652

Ⓗ 661

Ⓙ 662

4

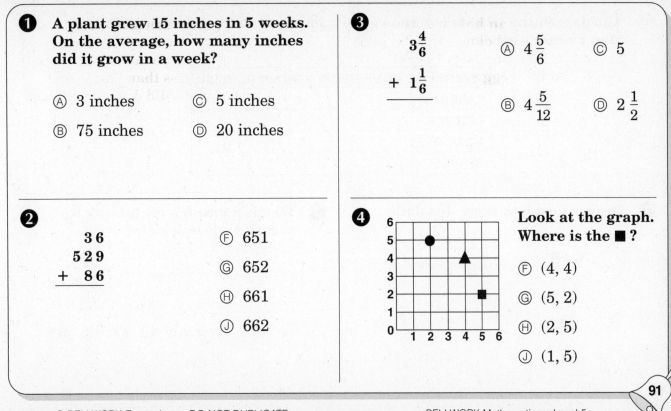

Look at the graph. Where is the ■ ?

Ⓕ (4, 4)

Ⓖ (5, 2)

Ⓗ (2, 5)

Ⓙ (1, 5)

BELLWORK Mathematics • Level 5

The data in the table below shows the number of plants growing in Mrs. Farmer's garden.

PLANTS	NUMBER GROWING IN GARDEN
CARROTS	10
LETTUCE	4
TOMATOES	8
BEANS	12

❶ Draw a graph to show this data.

❷ Why is a graph a useful way to record and show data?

1 A spinner was spun 100 times. The results are shown in the table below.

	W	X	Y	Z
Number of times the spinner landed on a letter.	10	25	50	15

Which spinner was most likely used?

Ⓐ

Ⓒ

Ⓑ

Ⓓ

2 A brick wall is being built. There are 40 bricks in the first row, 34 bricks in the second row, and 28 bricks in the third row. If this pattern continues, how many bricks will be in the fifth row?

Ⓕ 102 bricks   Ⓗ 22 bricks

Ⓖ 26 bricks   Ⓙ 16 bricks

Explain your answer.

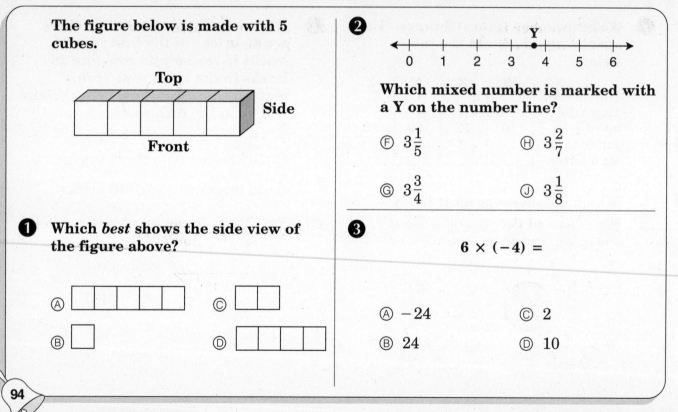

The figure below is made with 5 cubes.

Top

Side

Front

1 Which *best* shows the side view of the figure above?

Ⓐ

Ⓒ

Ⓑ

Ⓓ

2

Y

0 1 2 3 4 5 6

Which mixed number is marked with a Y on the number line?

Ⓕ $3\frac{1}{5}$ Ⓗ $3\frac{2}{7}$

Ⓖ $3\frac{3}{4}$ Ⓙ $3\frac{1}{8}$

3

$$6 \times (-4) =$$

Ⓐ -24 Ⓒ 2

Ⓑ 24   Ⓓ 10

Name _____

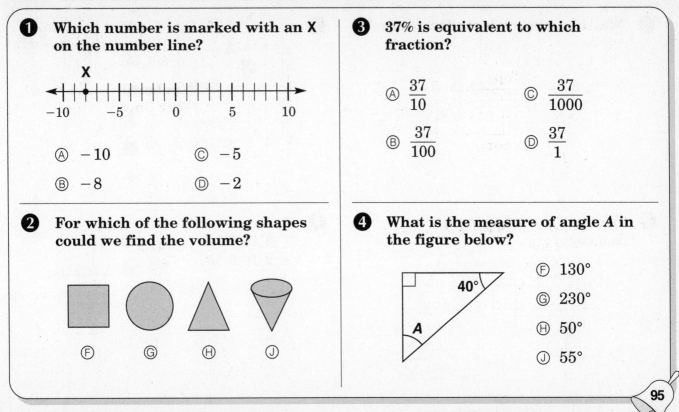

1 **Which number is marked with an X on the number line?**

X

-10   -5   0   5   10

(A) -10   (C) -5

(B) -8   (D) -2

2 **For which of the following shapes could we find the volume?**

(F)   (G)   (H)   (J)

3 **37% is equivalent to which fraction?**

(A) $\frac{37}{10}$ (C) $\frac{37}{1000}$

(B) $\frac{37}{100}$ (D) $\frac{37}{1}$

4 **What is the measure of angle A in the figure below?**

40°

A

(F) 130°

(G) 230°

(H) 50°

(J) 55°

1 **Which number has the least value?**

Ⓐ 0.16   Ⓒ 0.05

Ⓑ 1.75   Ⓓ 0.2

3 Look at the graph. What is located at (3, 5)?

Ⓐ ●

Ⓑ ▲

Ⓒ ■

Ⓓ ✚

2 **Which of the following figures is a cone?**

Ⓕ   Ⓗ

Ⓖ   Ⓙ

4

3 ft 7 in.
+ 2 ft 5 in.

Ⓕ 6 ft

Ⓖ 1 ft 2 in.

Ⓗ 5 ft 11 in.

Ⓙ 6 ft 2 in.

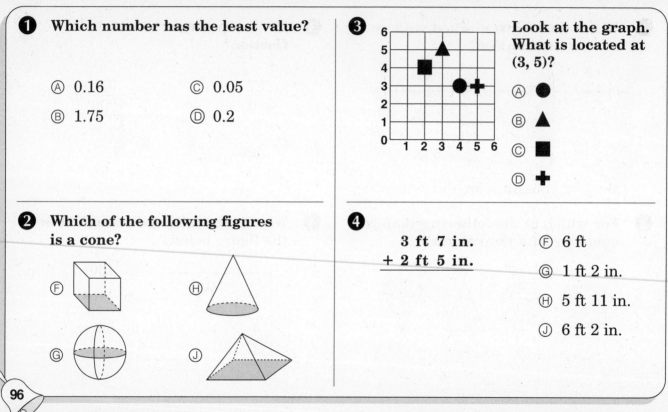

1 In the figure below, is the dotted line a line of symmetry?

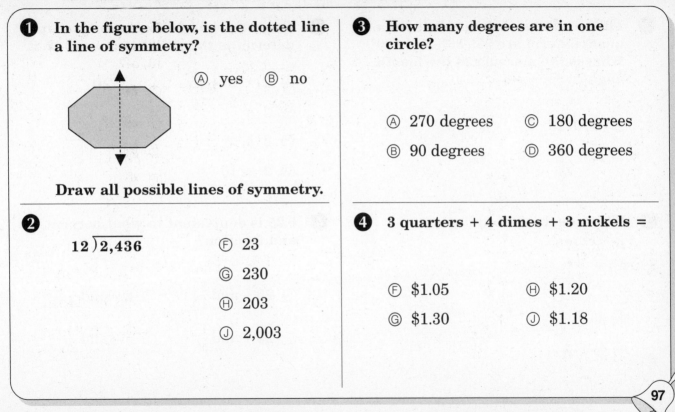

Ⓐ yes   Ⓑ no

Draw all possible lines of symmetry.

2

$$12\overline{)2,436}$$

Ⓕ 23

Ⓖ 230

Ⓗ 203

Ⓙ 2,003

3 How many degrees are in one circle?

Ⓐ 270 degrees   Ⓒ 180 degrees

Ⓑ 90 degrees   Ⓓ 360 degrees

4 3 quarters + 4 dimes + 3 nickels =

Ⓕ $1.05   Ⓗ $1.20

Ⓖ $1.30   Ⓙ $1.18

Name _____

1 The measures of three angles of a quadrilateral are 95°, 86°, and 100°. What is the measure of the fourth angle?

Ⓐ 234°   Ⓒ 79°

Ⓑ 19°   Ⓓ 90°

2 Which decimal is equivalent to $\frac{75}{1000}$?

Ⓕ 0.75   Ⓗ 7.5

Ⓖ 0.075   Ⓙ 75

3 Use the prime factorization tree to determine the prime factors of 20.

Ⓐ 2 × 2 × 5

Ⓑ 2 × 5

Ⓒ 2^3 × 5

Ⓓ 2 × 10

20

4 0.25 is equivalent to what percent and fraction?

Ⓕ 25% and $\frac{25}{10}$ Ⓗ 2% and $\frac{1}{4}$

Ⓖ 25% and $\frac{1}{4}$ Ⓙ 5% and $\frac{1}{25}$

Name _____

1 The area of this square is 36 cm². What is the area of one of the triangles?

Ⓐ 18 cm²

Ⓑ 12 cm²

Ⓒ 24 cm²

Ⓓ 20 cm²

6 cm

6 cm

2

$$-50 + (-25) =$$

Ⓕ 75

Ⓗ -75

Ⓖ -25

Ⓙ 25

3 What is 50% of 250?

Ⓐ 25

Ⓒ 110

Ⓑ 125

Ⓓ 375

4 Use the distributive property to help you solve for a.

What is the value of a?

$$5(a + 1) = 30$$

Ⓕ 7

Ⓗ 6

Ⓖ 5

Ⓙ 2

Name _____

1 **Reduce (simplify) to lowest terms:**

$$\frac{2}{4}$$

Ⓐ $\frac{4}{8}$ Ⓒ $\frac{1}{2}$

Ⓑ 1 Ⓓ 6

3 **Which figure is a pyramid?**

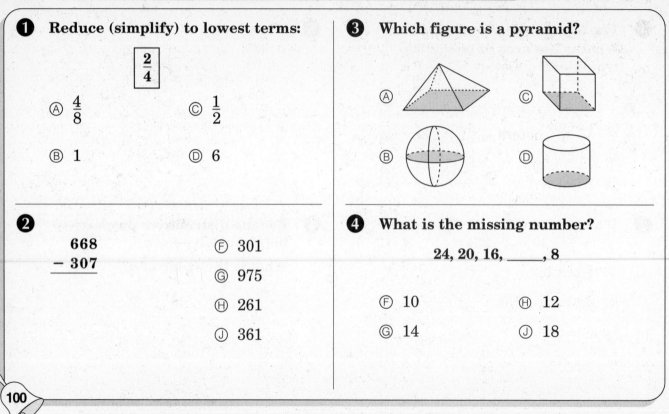

Ⓐ Ⓒ

Ⓑ Ⓓ

2

$$\begin{array}{r} 668 \\ -\ 307 \\ \hline \end{array}$$

Ⓕ 301

Ⓖ 975

Ⓗ 261

Ⓙ 361

4 **What is the missing number?**

24, 20, 16, _____, 8

Ⓕ 10 Ⓗ 12

Ⓖ 14 Ⓙ 18

100

1 **Find the area.**

5 meters

4 meters

Ⓐ 18 sq. meters   Ⓒ 20 sq. meters

Ⓑ 18 meters   Ⓓ 20 meters

2 **What is the value of the 3 in 64.31?**

Ⓕ 3 tenths

Ⓖ 3 hundredths

Ⓗ 3 ones

Ⓙ 3 tens

3

$$\begin{array}{r} 417 \\ \times\ \ 2 \\ \end{array}$$

Ⓐ 824

Ⓑ 419

Ⓒ 834

Ⓓ 934

4 **Reduce (simplify) to lowest terms:**

$$\frac{3}{6}$$

Ⓕ $\frac{1}{2}$ Ⓗ 9

Ⓖ $\frac{6}{12}$ Ⓙ $\frac{1}{3}$

BELLWORK Mathematics • Level 5

Name _____

1 **Which of the following arrays represents a prime number?**

Ⓐ ● ● ● ● ● ● ● ●

Ⓒ ● ●
● ●
● ●
● ●

Ⓑ ● ● ● ● ●
● ● ● ● ●
● ● ● ● ●

Ⓓ ● ● ● ● ● ●
● ● ● ● ● ●

2

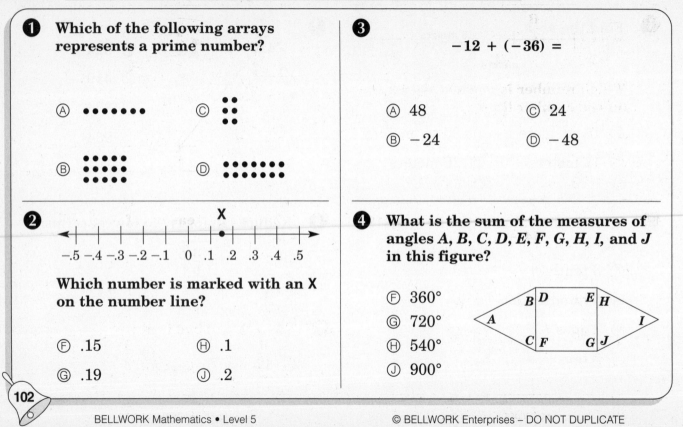

X

$-.5$ $-.4$ $-.3$ $-.2$ $-.1$ 0 $.1$ $.2$ $.3$ $.4$ $.5$

Which number is marked with an X on the number line?

Ⓕ .15   Ⓗ .1

Ⓖ .19   Ⓙ .2

3

$$-12 + (-36) =$$

Ⓐ 48   Ⓒ 24

Ⓑ -24 Ⓓ -48

4 **What is the sum of the measures of angles A, B, C, D, E, F, G, H, I, and J in this figure?**

Ⓕ 360°

Ⓖ 720°

Ⓗ 540°

Ⓙ 900°

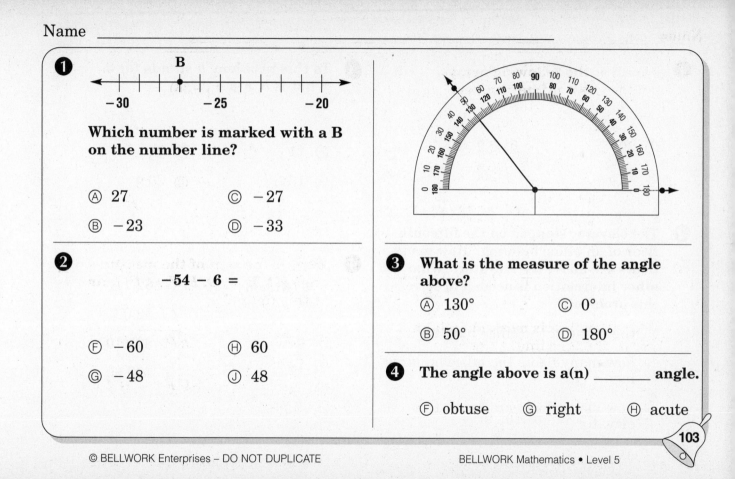

❶

B

−30 −25 −20

Which number is marked with a B on the number line?

Ⓐ 27   Ⓒ −27

Ⓑ −23   Ⓓ −33

❷

$$-54 - 6 =$$

Ⓕ −60   Ⓗ 60

Ⓖ −48   Ⓙ 48

❸ What is the measure of the angle above?

Ⓐ 130°   Ⓒ 0°

Ⓑ 50°   Ⓓ 180°

❹ The angle above is a(n) _____ angle.

Ⓕ obtuse   Ⓖ right   Ⓗ acute

103

Name _____

1

$$1.5 \div 0.75 =$$

Ⓐ 20 Ⓒ 0.2

Ⓑ 2 Ⓓ 200

2 The elevator stopped on the fifteenth floor of an office building. How many floors are above the elevator? What other information is needed to solve this problem?

Ⓕ the name of the office building

Ⓖ how many floors the office building has

Ⓗ how many floors are below the elevator

3 In this problem, b stands for 3. What is $b \times 6 + 2$?

Ⓐ 11 Ⓒ 24

Ⓑ 16 Ⓓ 20

4

$$6\,\overline{)\,\$12.66}$$

Ⓕ $2.11

Ⓖ $2.06

Ⓗ $21.10

Ⓙ $20.60

104

Name _____

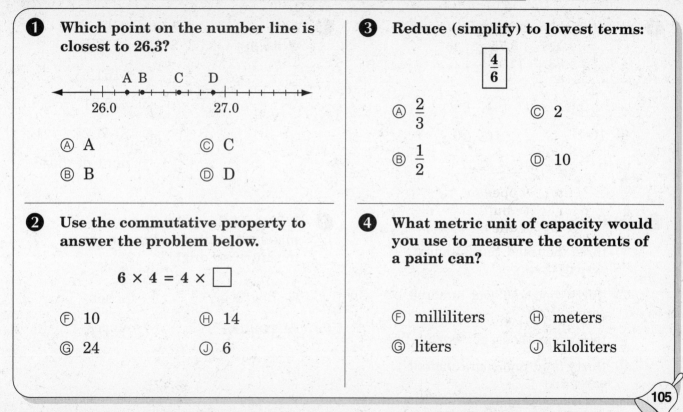

1 Which point on the number line is closest to 26.3?

A B   C   D

26.0   27.0

Ⓐ A

Ⓒ C

Ⓑ B

Ⓓ D

2 Use the commutative property to answer the problem below.

$$6 \times 4 = 4 \times \square$$

Ⓕ 10

Ⓗ 14

Ⓖ 24

Ⓙ 6

3 Reduce (simplify) to lowest terms:

$$\frac{4}{6}$$

Ⓐ $\frac{2}{3}$

Ⓒ 2

Ⓑ $\frac{1}{2}$

Ⓓ 10

4 What metric unit of capacity would you use to measure the contents of a paint can?

Ⓕ milliliters

Ⓗ meters

Ⓖ liters

Ⓙ kiloliters

Name _____

1 **What is the estimated answer?**

$$63 \div 11 = \square$$

(A) 10 (C) 9

(B) 6 (D) 7

2 **30,475 is read as:**

(F) three thousand, four hundred seventy-five

(G) thirty thousand, four hundred seventy-five

(H) thirty-four thousand, seventy-five

(J) thirty thousand, four hundred seven five

3

$$\begin{array}{r} \$\ 81.38 \\ -\ 70.17 \\ \hline \end{array}$$

(A) $11.31

(B) $151.55

(C) $10.21

(D) $141.21

(E) none of these

4 **Which of the following units of measurement should you use to measure an angle?**

(F) degrees (H) inches

(G) pounds (J) ounces

Name _____

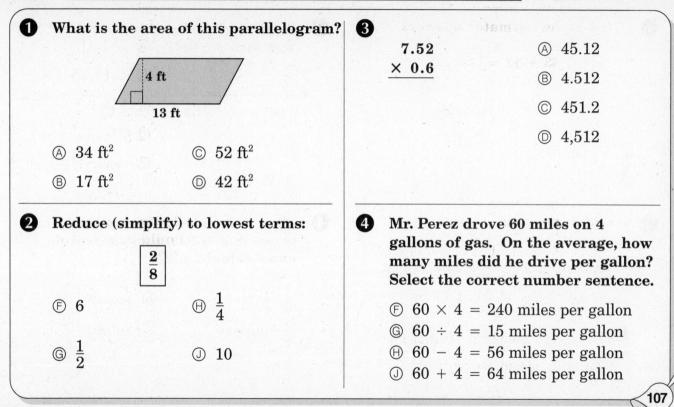

① **What is the area of this parallelogram?**

4 ft

13 ft

Ⓐ 34 ft²   Ⓒ 52 ft²

Ⓑ 17 ft²   Ⓓ 42 ft²

② **Reduce (simplify) to lowest terms:**

$$\frac{2}{8}$$

Ⓕ 6   Ⓗ $\frac{1}{4}$

Ⓖ $\frac{1}{2}$ Ⓙ 10

③

$$\begin{array}{r} 7.52 \\ \times\ 0.6 \\ \hline \end{array}$$

Ⓐ 45.12

Ⓑ 4.512

Ⓒ 451.2

Ⓓ 4,512

④ **Mr. Perez drove 60 miles on 4 gallons of gas. On the average, how many miles did he drive per gallon? Select the correct number sentence.**

Ⓕ 60 × 4 = 240 miles per gallon

Ⓖ 60 ÷ 4 = 15 miles per gallon

Ⓗ 60 − 4 = 56 miles per gallon

Ⓙ 60 + 4 = 64 miles per gallon

107

Name _____

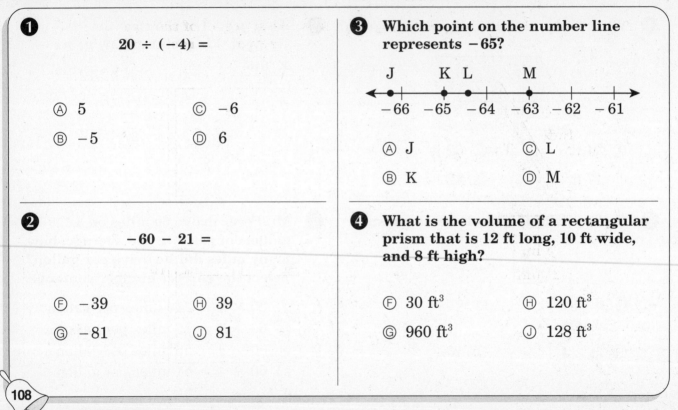

1

$$20 \div (-4) =$$

Ⓐ 5　　　　　Ⓒ −6

Ⓑ −5　　　　Ⓓ 6

2

$$-60 - 21 =$$

Ⓕ −39　　　　Ⓗ 39

Ⓖ −81　　　　Ⓙ 81

3 **Which point on the number line represents −65?**

J　　　K L　　　M

−66　−65　−64　−63　−62　−61

Ⓐ J　　　　　Ⓒ L

Ⓑ K　　　　　Ⓓ M

4 **What is the volume of a rectangular prism that is 12 ft long, 10 ft wide, and 8 ft high?**

Ⓕ 30 ft³　　　　Ⓗ 120 ft³

Ⓖ 960 ft³　　　　Ⓙ 128 ft³

Name _____

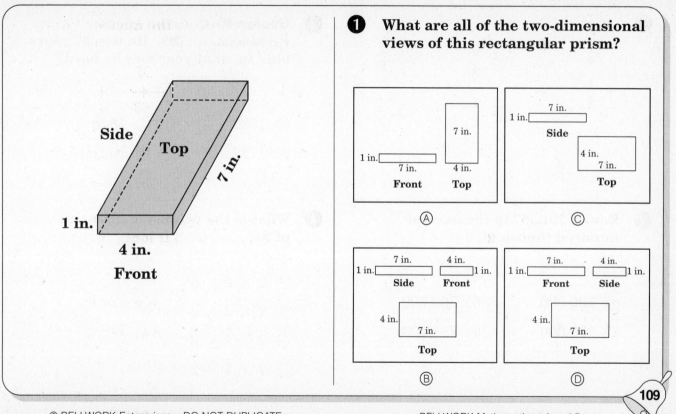

Side **Top** 7 in.

1 in.

4 in.

Front

1 **What are all of the two-dimensional views of this rectangular prism?**

Ⓐ
- 1 in. 7 in. **Front**
- 7 in. 4 in. **Top**

Ⓒ
- 7 in. 1 in. **Side**
- 4 in. 7 in. **Top**

Ⓑ
- 1 in. 7 in. **Side** 4 in. 1 in. **Front**
- 4 in. 7 in. **Top**

Ⓓ
- 1 in. 7 in. **Front** 4 in. 1 in. **Side**
- 4 in. 7 in. **Top**

Name _____

❶

$$\frac{1}{4}$$
$$+\ \frac{1}{4}$$

Ⓐ $\frac{0}{4}$ Ⓒ $\frac{2}{8}$

Ⓑ $\frac{1}{2}$ Ⓓ $\frac{1}{16}$

❸ George Washington became President in 1789. He was 57 years old. In what year was he born?

Ⓐ 1732   Ⓒ 1846

Ⓑ 1722   Ⓓ 1022

❷ Round 791,367 to the nearest hundred thousand.

Ⓕ 700,000   Ⓗ 790,000

Ⓖ 800,000   Ⓙ 791,400

❹ What is the prime factorization of 24?

Ⓕ $2 \times 2 \times 6$

Ⓖ $2 \times 2 \times 2 \times 3$

Ⓗ $2 \times 2 \times 3$

Ⓙ $2 \times 2 \times 2 \times 6$

Name _____

❶

$$32 + 10 = \boxed{}$$

Ⓐ 8×3 Ⓒ $42 \div 2$

Ⓑ 7×6 Ⓓ $37 \div 5$

❷

$$\begin{array}{r} 351 \\ \times\ 45 \\ \hline \end{array}$$

Ⓕ 15,795

Ⓖ 3,159

Ⓗ 396

Ⓙ 13,795

❸

$$\frac{1}{9} \div \frac{1}{4} =$$

Ⓐ $\dfrac{1}{36}$ Ⓒ $\dfrac{9}{4}$

Ⓑ $\dfrac{4}{9}$ Ⓓ $\dfrac{2}{13}$

❹

$$\frac{1}{3} \qquad \frac{1}{4} \qquad \boxed{\frac{1}{8}}$$

Of the three fractions shown above, the one that is circled has —

Ⓕ the greatest value.

Ⓖ the least value.

Ⓗ the same value.

BELLWORK Mathematics • Level 5

1 Abraham Lincoln became President in 1861. He was 52 years old. In what year was he born?

Ⓐ 1809 Ⓒ 1913

Ⓑ 1811 Ⓓ 1709

2 A certain cake recipe calls for 1 cup of sugar and 3 cups of flour. What is the ratio of sugar to flour?

Ⓕ $\frac{3}{1}$ Ⓗ $\frac{1}{3}$

Ⓖ $\frac{2}{3}$ Ⓙ $\frac{4}{3}$

3 Which number is divisible by 2, 4, and 5?

Ⓐ 12 Ⓒ 20

Ⓑ 16 Ⓓ 24

4

$$\frac{4}{5}$$
$$-\frac{3}{10}$$

Ⓕ $\frac{1}{2}$ Ⓗ $\frac{1}{15}$

Ⓖ $\frac{1}{5}$ Ⓙ $\frac{1}{10}$

❶

$$\frac{4}{6}$$

$$-\frac{1}{6}$$

Ⓐ $\frac{5}{6}$ Ⓒ $\frac{1}{2}$

Ⓑ $\frac{1}{3}$ Ⓓ $\frac{1}{6}$

❷

$$-7 - 5 =$$

Ⓕ -2 Ⓗ 2

Ⓖ -12 Ⓙ 12

❸ **Which number sentence goes with**
$21 \div 7 = \square$?

Ⓐ $\square + 7 = 21$

Ⓑ $\square \times 7 = 21$

Ⓒ $21 - \square = 7$

Ⓓ $21 + \square = 7$

❹

$$3{,}058.15$$
$$-\ 214.69$$

Ⓕ $2{,}843.46$

Ⓖ $2{,}844.46$

Ⓗ $3{,}244.54$

Ⓙ $2{,}843.56$

Ⓚ none of these

113

❶

$ 58.30
+   9.48

Ⓐ $67.40

Ⓑ $67.78

Ⓒ $57.78

Ⓓ $48.82

❸ In this problem, *a* stands for 2.
What is $3 \times 5 - a$?

Ⓐ 9

Ⓑ 13

Ⓒ 6

Ⓓ 17

❷

    154
×   16

Ⓕ 2,374

Ⓖ 2,464

Ⓗ 2,364

Ⓙ 1,078

❹ Which list has the numbers in order
from greatest value to least value?

Ⓕ 5.41, 5.46, 5.23, 5.19

Ⓖ 5.46, 5.41, 5.23, 5.19

Ⓗ 5.46, 5.41, 5.19, 5.23

Ⓙ 5.19, 5.23, 5.46, 5.41

Name _____

❶

$$0.5 \times 0.5 =$$

Ⓐ 2.5   Ⓒ 25

Ⓑ 0.25   Ⓓ 0.025

❷

$$15\overline{)1{,}545}$$

Ⓕ 103

Ⓖ 130

Ⓗ 13

Ⓙ 1,030

❸ Which drawing, when folded on the dotted lines, could form the rectangular prism on the right?

Ⓐ   Ⓑ   Ⓒ   Ⓓ

❹

$$4\tfrac{3}{4}$$
$$-\,2\tfrac{1}{6}$$

Ⓕ $2\tfrac{2}{12}$ Ⓗ $2\tfrac{7}{12}$

Ⓖ $6\tfrac{11}{12}$ Ⓙ $\tfrac{7}{12}$

Name _____

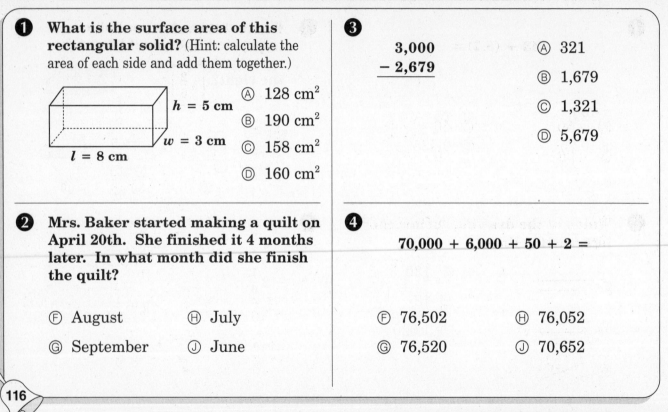

1 **What is the surface area of this rectangular solid?** (Hint: calculate the area of each side and add them together.)

$h = 5$ cm

$w = 3$ cm

$l = 8$ cm

Ⓐ 128 cm^2

Ⓑ 190 cm^2

Ⓒ 158 cm^2

Ⓓ 160 cm^2

2 **Mrs. Baker started making a quilt on April 20th. She finished it 4 months later. In what month did she finish the quilt?**

Ⓕ August

Ⓗ July

Ⓖ September

Ⓙ June

3

$$\begin{array}{r} 3,000 \\ -\ 2,679 \end{array}$$

Ⓐ 321

Ⓑ 1,679

Ⓒ 1,321

Ⓓ 5,679

4

$$70,000 + 6,000 + 50 + 2 =$$

Ⓕ 76,502

Ⓗ 76,052

Ⓖ 76,520

Ⓙ 70,652

Name _____

❶

$$-43 + (-7) =$$

(A) -50 (C) 50

(B) -36 (D) 36

❷ **Which of the drawings below shows intersecting lines?**

(F) ⟷⟷

(G) ⟷⟷

(H) ✕

❸ **Convert the mixed number to an improper fraction.**

$$4\frac{2}{5}$$

(A) $\dfrac{20}{5}$ (C) $\dfrac{22}{5}$

(B) $\dfrac{22}{2}$ (D) $\dfrac{20}{2}$

❹

$$\frac{1}{2} \cdot \frac{1}{3} =$$

(F) $\dfrac{2}{6}$ (H) $\dfrac{1}{6}$

(G) $\dfrac{1}{5}$ (J) $\dfrac{3}{2}$

117

Name _____

❶

$$4^5 = \square$$

Ⓐ 4×5

Ⓑ $4 \times 4 \times 4 \times 4 \times 4$

Ⓒ $5 \times 5 \times 5 \times 5$

Ⓓ $4 \div 5$

❷ **The rectangle to the right is divided into two triangles.**

```
90°        Z
   \
    \
     \
      \
40°      90°
```

What is the measure of ∠ Z?

Ⓕ 40°   Ⓗ 45°

Ⓖ 50°   Ⓙ 130°

❸ **The <u>perimeter</u> of a playground should be measured using which unit of measurement?**

Ⓐ yd   Ⓒ yd^3

Ⓑ yd^2 Ⓓ in.

❹

$$-45 - 23 =$$

Ⓕ -22 Ⓗ 68

Ⓖ -68 Ⓙ 22

College Campus Buildings

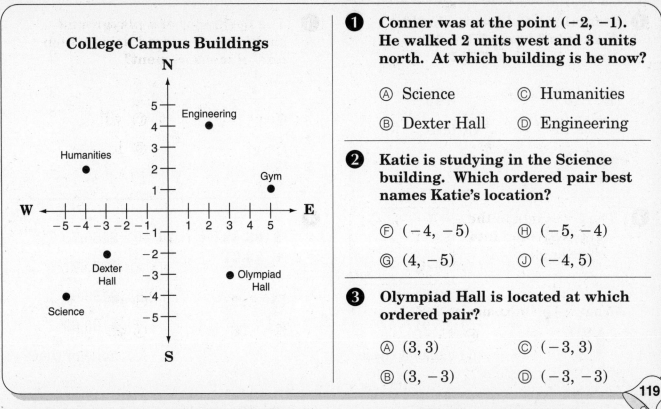

1 Conner was at the point (−2, −1). He walked 2 units west and 3 units north. At which building is he now?

Ⓐ Science Ⓒ Humanities

Ⓑ Dexter Hall Ⓓ Engineering

2 Katie is studying in the Science building. Which ordered pair best names Katie's location?

Ⓕ (−4, −5) Ⓗ (−5, −4)

Ⓖ (4, −5) Ⓙ (−4, 5)

3 Olympiad Hall is located at which ordered pair?

Ⓐ (3, 3) Ⓒ (−3, 3)

Ⓑ (3, −3) Ⓓ (−3, −3)

1 It is 3:15 in California. In New York it is 3 hours later. What time is it in New York?

Ⓐ 1:15   Ⓒ 6:45

Ⓑ 12:15   Ⓓ 6:15

3

$$\frac{3}{4} - \frac{1}{4}$$

Ⓐ $\frac{1}{4}$ Ⓒ $\frac{1}{2}$

Ⓑ 1   Ⓓ $\frac{3}{8}$

2

$8\overline{)\$72.08}$

Ⓕ $9.11

Ⓖ $9.01

Ⓗ $9.91

Ⓙ $8.01

Ⓚ none of these

4

$$\$\ 86.48 + 73.21$$

Ⓕ $160.70

Ⓖ $13.27

Ⓗ $159.69

Ⓙ $160.69

Ⓚ none of these

Name _____

1 Which of the figures below is <u>not</u> a hexagon?

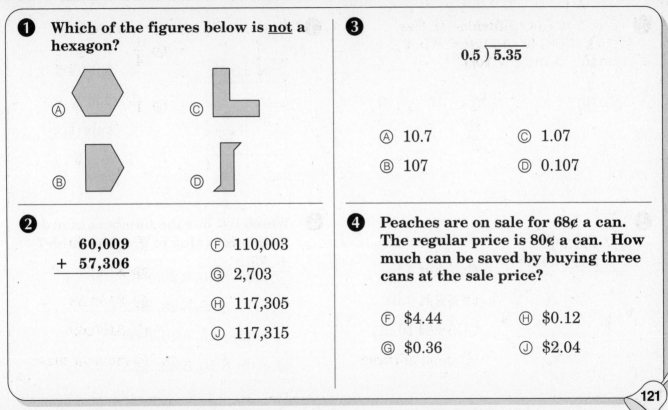

Ⓐ

Ⓒ

Ⓑ

Ⓓ

2

$$60,009$$
$$+\ 57,306$$

Ⓕ 110,003

Ⓖ 2,703

Ⓗ 117,305

Ⓙ 117,315

3

$$0.5\overline{)5.35}$$

Ⓐ 10.7   Ⓒ 1.07

Ⓑ 107   Ⓓ 0.107

4 Peaches are on sale for 68¢ a can. The regular price is 80¢ a can. How much can be saved by buying three cans at the sale price?

Ⓕ $4.44   Ⓗ $0.12

Ⓖ $0.36   Ⓙ $2.04

121

Name _____

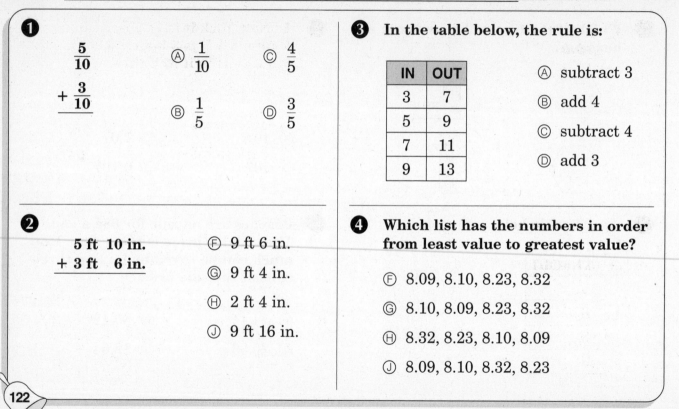

1

$\dfrac{5}{10}$

$+ \dfrac{3}{10}$

Ⓐ $\dfrac{1}{10}$ Ⓒ $\dfrac{4}{5}$

Ⓑ $\dfrac{1}{5}$ Ⓓ $\dfrac{3}{5}$

2

   5 ft 10 in.

+ 3 ft   6 in.

Ⓕ 9 ft 6 in.

Ⓖ 9 ft 4 in.

Ⓗ 2 ft 4 in.

Ⓙ 9 ft 16 in.

3 **In the table below, the rule is:**

IN	OUT
3	7
5	9
7	11
9	13

Ⓐ subtract 3

Ⓑ add 4

Ⓒ subtract 4

Ⓓ add 3

4 **Which list has the numbers in order from least value to greatest value?**

Ⓕ 8.09, 8.10, 8.23, 8.32

Ⓖ 8.10, 8.09, 8.23, 8.32

Ⓗ 8.32, 8.23, 8.10, 8.09

Ⓙ 8.09, 8.10, 8.32, 8.23

122

❶

$$38.5$$
$$+ \ 40.5$$

Ⓐ 78.5

Ⓑ 79

Ⓒ 89

Ⓓ 78

❸ **In New York it is 1:00 p.m. In California it is 3 hours earlier. What time is it in California?**

Ⓐ 10:00 a.m.　　Ⓒ 4:00 p.m.

Ⓑ 11:00 a.m.　　Ⓓ 10:00 p.m.

❷ **In the table below, the rule is:**

IN	OUT
4	8
6	12
8	16
10	20

Ⓕ add 4

Ⓖ subtract 6

Ⓗ multiply by 2

Ⓙ divide by 2

❹

$$\frac{1}{3} \div \frac{1}{2} =$$

Ⓕ $\frac{1}{6}$　　　　Ⓗ $\frac{1}{5}$

Ⓖ $\frac{2}{3}$　　　　Ⓙ $\frac{3}{2}$

123

Name _____

1 Adam can make 3 hops for every 10 yards he travels. How many yards must he travel to make 24 hops? Use the table to help you find the answer.

Hops	3	6	9							
Yards traveled	10	20	30	40						

Ⓐ 72 yards   Ⓒ 80 yards

Ⓑ 70 yards   Ⓓ 240 yards

2 James bought 24 hot dogs for his beach barbeque. His friends ate $\frac{3}{4}$ of them. How many hot dogs did they eat?

Ⓕ 12 hot dogs   Ⓗ 22 hot dogs

Ⓖ 16 hot dogs   Ⓙ 18 hot dogs

3 Rearrange the digits 3, 5, and 6 to make as many different three-digit numbers as you can.

Name _____

José drives his car to work every morning. The graph below shows the time and distance for his drive. Use the graph to answer the following questions.

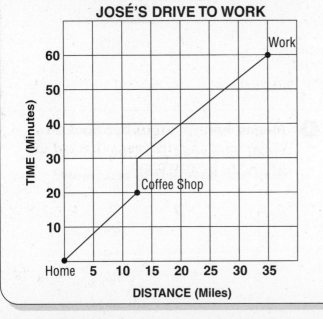

JOSÉ'S DRIVE TO WORK

1 About how many miles did José drive in the first 40 minutes?

Ⓐ 15 miles Ⓒ 25 miles

Ⓑ 20 miles Ⓓ 30 miles

2 José stopped to get coffee on his way to work. About how many minutes did it take him to go from home to the coffee shop?

Ⓕ 10 minutes Ⓗ 20 minutes

Ⓖ 15 minutes Ⓙ 30 minutes

3 If José didn't stop for coffee, about how long would it take him to travel from home to work?

Ⓐ 30 minutes Ⓒ 40 minutes

Ⓑ 60 minutes Ⓓ 50 minutes

125

Name _____

1

$$\frac{7}{8}$$
$$-\frac{1}{16}$$

Ⓐ $\frac{6}{8}$ Ⓒ $\frac{6}{16}$

Ⓑ $\frac{13}{16}$ Ⓓ $\frac{15}{16}$

3

$16\overline{)484}$

Ⓐ 30.25

Ⓑ 3.025

Ⓒ 302.5

Ⓓ 325

2 There were 12 ice-cream bars in the freezer. Half of them were eaten. How many are left?

Ⓕ 6 bars   Ⓗ 4 bars

Ⓖ 8 bars   Ⓙ 10 bars

4 Megan had $\frac{7}{12}$ left of her book to read. She read $\frac{5}{12}$. How much does she have left to read now?

Ⓕ 1   Ⓗ $\frac{2}{24}$

Ⓖ $\frac{1}{6}$ Ⓙ $\frac{12}{24}$

Name _____

❶

$$-150 + (-50) =$$

Ⓐ 100   Ⓒ 200

Ⓑ −100   Ⓓ −200

❸ Reduce (simplify) to lowest terms:

$$\boxed{\dfrac{4}{16}}$$

Ⓐ $\dfrac{1}{4}$ Ⓒ $\dfrac{1}{8}$

Ⓑ 4   Ⓓ $\dfrac{2}{4}$

❷ **Look at the table. The missing number is _____.**

IN	OUT
12	8
10	6
8	
6	2

Ⓕ 3

Ⓖ 5

Ⓗ 4

Ⓙ 6

❹

$$0.9 \times 0.1 =$$

Ⓕ 9.0   Ⓗ 0.09

Ⓖ 0.9   Ⓙ 0.009

127

①

$$163 - (-39) =$$

Ⓐ −124   Ⓒ −202

Ⓑ 124   Ⓓ 202

②

$$\frac{2}{3}$$
$$+ \frac{1}{9}$$

Ⓕ $\frac{6}{9}$ Ⓗ $\frac{7}{9}$

Ⓖ $\frac{3}{12}$ Ⓙ $\frac{7}{18}$

③ What is the measure of ∠Y in the figure below?

Ⓐ 125°   Ⓒ 65°

Ⓑ 235°   Ⓓ 35°

④ Maggie has $\frac{1}{2}$ yard of purple fabric. She needs to cut $\frac{1}{3}$ of what she has. Which number sentence should she use to figure out how much to cut?

Ⓕ $\frac{1}{2} \div \frac{1}{3}$ Ⓗ $\frac{1}{2} + \frac{1}{3}$

Ⓖ $\frac{1}{2} \times \frac{1}{3}$

1 **Complete the prime factorization tree.**

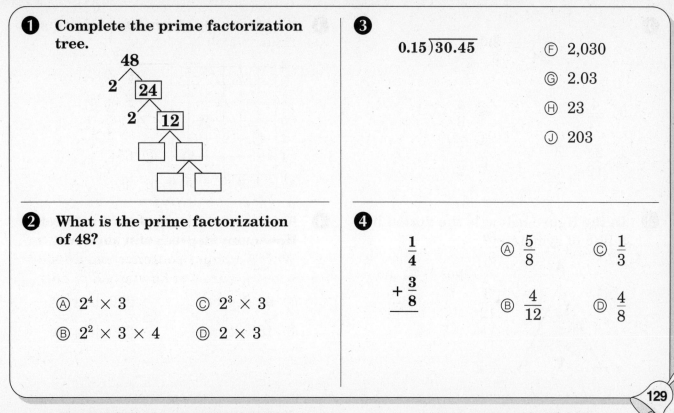

2 **What is the prime factorization of 48?**

Ⓐ $2^4 \times 3$ Ⓒ $2^3 \times 3$

Ⓑ $2^2 \times 3 \times 4$ Ⓓ 2×3

3

$0.15 \overline{)30.45}$

Ⓕ 2,030

Ⓖ 2.03

Ⓗ 23

Ⓙ 203

4

$$\begin{array}{r} \frac{1}{4} \\ + \frac{3}{8} \\ \hline \end{array}$$

Ⓐ $\frac{5}{8}$ Ⓒ $\frac{1}{3}$

Ⓑ $\frac{4}{12}$ Ⓓ $\frac{4}{8}$

129

Name _____

1
$$\frac{4}{24} \div \frac{1}{3} =$$

Ⓐ $\frac{4}{72}$ Ⓒ $\frac{4}{6}$

Ⓑ $\frac{24}{12}$ Ⓓ $\frac{1}{2}$

2 In the figure below, is the dotted line a line of symmetry?

Ⓕ yes   Ⓖ no

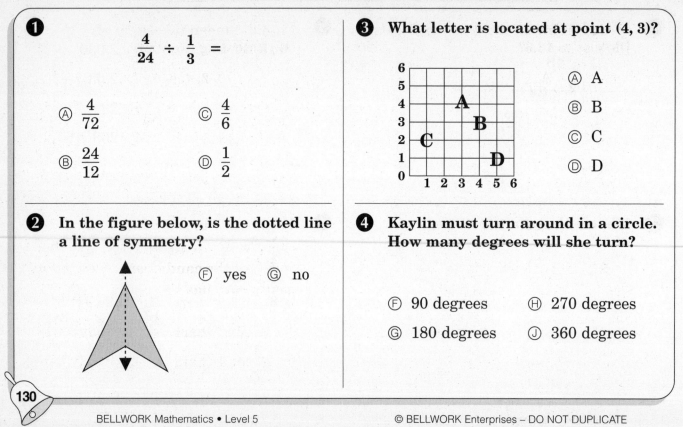

3 What letter is located at point (4, 3)?

Ⓐ A

Ⓑ B

Ⓒ C

Ⓓ D

4 Kaylin must turn around in a circle. How many degrees will she turn?

Ⓕ 90 degrees   Ⓗ 270 degrees

Ⓖ 180 degrees   Ⓙ 360 degrees

Name _____

1 **Which point on the number line is closest to 13.6?**

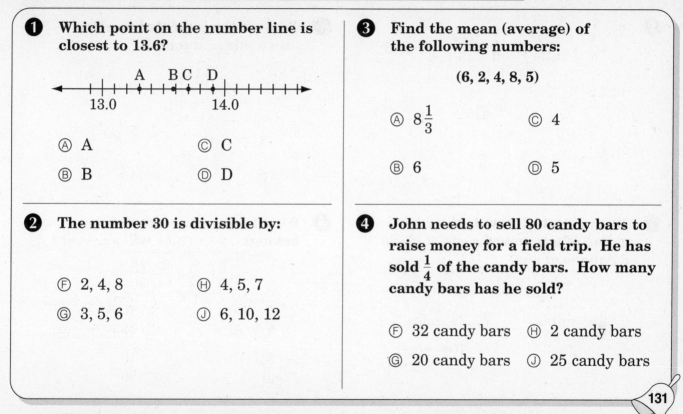

(A) A   (C) C

(B) B   (D) D

2 **The number 30 is divisible by:**

(F) 2, 4, 8   (H) 4, 5, 7

(G) 3, 5, 6   (J) 6, 10, 12

3 **Find the mean (average) of the following numbers:**

(6, 2, 4, 8, 5)

(A) $8\frac{1}{3}$ (C) 4

(B) 6   (D) 5

4 **John needs to sell 80 candy bars to raise money for a field trip. He has sold $\frac{1}{4}$ of the candy bars. How many candy bars has he sold?**

(F) 32 candy bars   (H) 2 candy bars

(G) 20 candy bars   (J) 25 candy bars

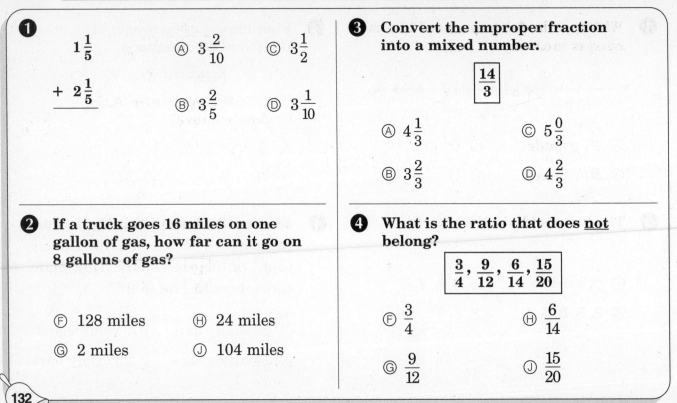

1

$1\frac{1}{5}$

$+ \ 2\frac{1}{5}$

Ⓐ $3\frac{2}{10}$　　Ⓒ $3\frac{1}{2}$

Ⓑ $3\frac{2}{5}$　　Ⓓ $3\frac{1}{10}$

2 If a truck goes 16 miles on one gallon of gas, how far can it go on 8 gallons of gas?

Ⓕ 128 miles　　Ⓗ 24 miles

Ⓖ 2 miles　　Ⓙ 104 miles

3 Convert the improper fraction into a mixed number.

$$\boxed{\dfrac{14}{3}}$$

Ⓐ $4\frac{1}{3}$　　Ⓒ $5\frac{0}{3}$

Ⓑ $3\frac{2}{3}$　　Ⓓ $4\frac{2}{3}$

4 What is the ratio that does <u>not</u> belong?

$$\boxed{\frac{3}{4},\ \frac{9}{12},\ \frac{6}{14},\ \frac{15}{20}}$$

Ⓕ $\frac{3}{4}$　　Ⓗ $\frac{6}{14}$

Ⓖ $\frac{9}{12}$　　Ⓙ $\frac{15}{20}$

Name _____

1 Which of the following could be the correct measure for angle *x*?

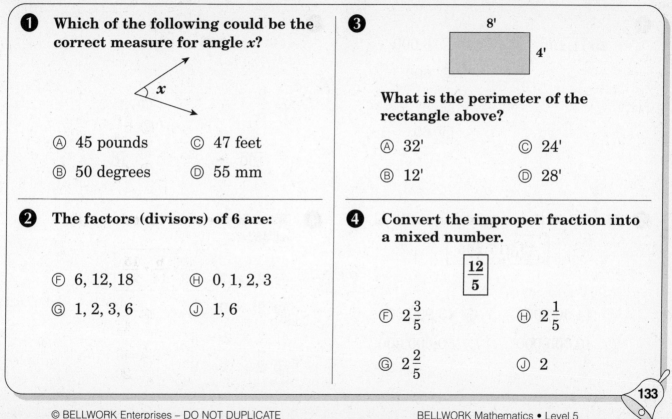

(A) 45 pounds   (C) 47 feet

(B) 50 degrees   (D) 55 mm

2 The factors (divisors) of 6 are:

(F) 6, 12, 18   (H) 0, 1, 2, 3

(G) 1, 2, 3, 6   (J) 1, 6

3

8'

4'

What is the perimeter of the rectangle above?

(A) 32'   (C) 24'

(B) 12'   (D) 28'

4 Convert the improper fraction into a mixed number.

$$\frac{12}{5}$$

(F) $2\frac{3}{5}$ (H) $2\frac{1}{5}$

(G) $2\frac{2}{5}$ (J) 2

133

1

$20 \overline{)1{,}200}$

Ⓐ 6,000

Ⓑ 600

Ⓒ 6

Ⓓ 60

3

$0.25 = \boxed{}$

Ⓐ $\dfrac{2}{5}$ Ⓒ 25%

Ⓑ $\dfrac{52}{100}$ Ⓓ $\dfrac{25}{10}$

2 **Round to the nearest ten million.**

43,917,206

Ⓕ 44,000,000   Ⓗ 43,900,000

Ⓖ 40,000,000   Ⓙ 50,000,000

4 **What is the prime factorization of 36?**

Ⓕ $2^2 \times 3^2$

Ⓖ $2^2 \times 9$

Ⓗ $2 \times 2 \times 3$

Ⓙ $2 \times 3 \times 6$

Name _____

❶ Which percent is equivalent to the fraction $\frac{10}{100}$?

Ⓐ 1%　　Ⓒ 11%

Ⓑ 10%　　Ⓓ 110%

❷ What is the prime factorization of 40?

Ⓕ $2 \times 4 \times 5$

Ⓖ $2 \times 2 \times 10$

Ⓗ $2 \times 2 \times 5$

Ⓙ $2 \times 2 \times 2 \times 5$

❸ Round to the nearest million.

$$27,856,242$$

Ⓐ 27,000,000　　Ⓒ 27,900,000

Ⓑ 30,000,000　　Ⓓ 28,000,000

❹

$$-20 - 5 =$$

Ⓕ -15　　Ⓗ 15

Ⓖ -25　　Ⓙ 25

1 **What is the value of the 8 in 83,604?**

Ⓐ 8 thousands

Ⓑ 8 ten thousands

Ⓒ 8 hundred thousands

Ⓓ 8 millions

Ⓔ none of these

2 **Use the distributive property to simplify the expression below.**

$$2(x - 9)$$

Ⓕ $2 - x - 7$ Ⓗ $2x - 18$

Ⓖ $2x - 7$ Ⓙ $2x - 11$

3 **Round $12\frac{1}{8}$ inches to the nearest inch.**

Ⓐ 11 inches   Ⓒ 13 inches

Ⓑ 12 inches   Ⓓ 10 inches

4 **The factors (divisors) of 8 are:**

Ⓕ 2, 4, 8   Ⓗ 1, 2, 4, 8

Ⓖ 0, 2, 4, 8   Ⓙ 8, 16, 24

Name _____

1 Ty rode his bicycle for 4 hours traveling about 19 miles per hour. *Estimate* how many miles he traveled in the 4 hours.

Ⓐ 60 miles   Ⓒ 80 miles

Ⓑ 70 miles   Ⓓ 90 miles

2

$4) \overline{\$2.52}$

Ⓕ $6.30

Ⓖ $6.40

Ⓗ $0.63

Ⓙ $0.64

3 In the space below, draw an array for 4 × 5.

4 The factors (divisors) of 5 are:

Ⓐ 5, 10, 15   Ⓒ 1, 5

Ⓑ 0, 1, 5   Ⓓ 1, 2, 5

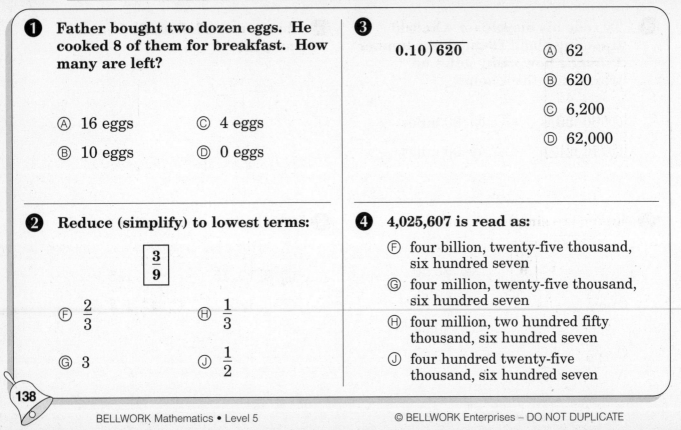

1 Father bought two dozen eggs. He cooked 8 of them for breakfast. How many are left?

Ⓐ 16 eggs   Ⓒ 4 eggs

Ⓑ 10 eggs   Ⓓ 0 eggs

2 Reduce (simplify) to lowest terms:

$$\frac{3}{9}$$

Ⓕ $\frac{2}{3}$ Ⓗ $\frac{1}{3}$

Ⓖ 3   Ⓙ $\frac{1}{2}$

3

$0.10\overline{)620}$

Ⓐ 62

Ⓑ 620

Ⓒ 6,200

Ⓓ 62,000

4 4,025,607 is read as:

Ⓕ four billion, twenty-five thousand, six hundred seven

Ⓖ four million, twenty-five thousand, six hundred seven

Ⓗ four million, two hundred fifty thousand, six hundred seven

Ⓙ four hundred twenty-five thousand, six hundred seven

Name _____

Name _____

1 Look at the table.
The missing number
is ____.

IN	OUT
9	
7	42
6	36
0	0

Ⓐ 56

Ⓑ 63

Ⓒ 45

Ⓓ 54

2 Reduce to simplest terms.

$$\boxed{\frac{38}{9}}$$

Ⓕ $4\frac{3}{9}$

Ⓗ $4\frac{1}{3}$

Ⓖ $4\frac{2}{9}$

Ⓙ $4\frac{1}{9}$

3 Which pair of shapes below are
congruent?

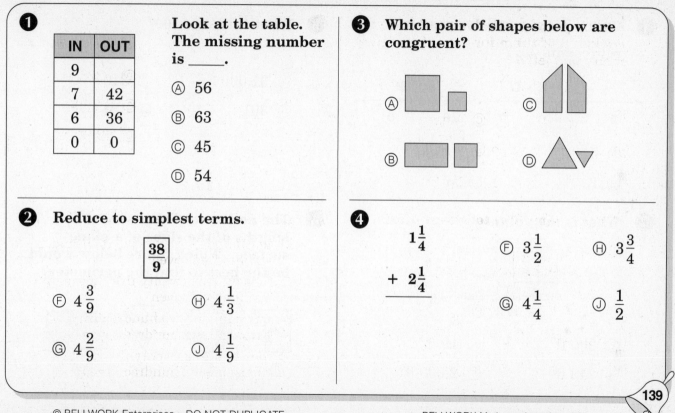

Ⓐ

Ⓒ

Ⓑ

Ⓓ

4

$$1\frac{1}{4}$$
$$+\ 2\frac{1}{4}$$

Ⓕ $3\frac{1}{2}$

Ⓗ $3\frac{3}{4}$

Ⓖ $4\frac{1}{4}$

Ⓙ $\frac{1}{2}$

Name _____

1 **Which point on the number line represents $6\frac{1}{4}$?**

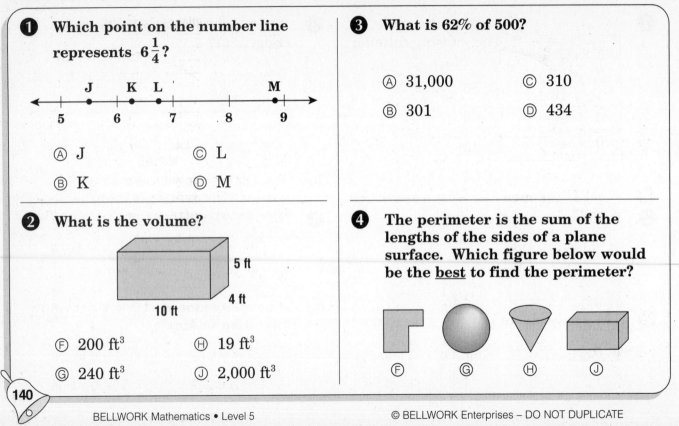

Ⓐ J

Ⓒ L

Ⓑ K

Ⓓ M

2 **What is the volume?**

5 ft

4 ft

10 ft

Ⓕ 200 ft³

Ⓗ 19 ft³

Ⓖ 240 ft³

Ⓙ 2,000 ft³

3 **What is 62% of 500?**

Ⓐ 31,000

Ⓒ 310

Ⓑ 301

Ⓓ 434

4 **The perimeter is the sum of the lengths of the sides of a plane surface. Which figure below would be the <u>best</u> to find the perimeter?**

Ⓕ

Ⓖ

Ⓗ

Ⓙ

Name _____

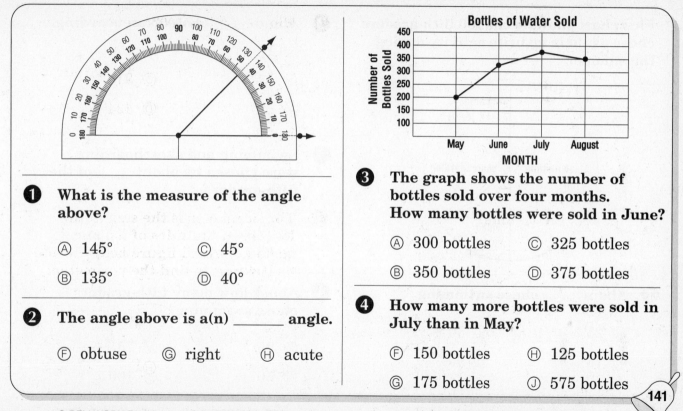

Bottles of Water Sold

❶ What is the measure of the angle above?

Ⓐ 145° Ⓒ 45°

Ⓑ 135° Ⓓ 40°

❷ The angle above is a(n) _____ angle.

Ⓕ obtuse Ⓖ right Ⓗ acute

❸ The graph shows the number of bottles sold over four months. How many bottles were sold in June?

Ⓐ 300 bottles Ⓒ 325 bottles

Ⓑ 350 bottles Ⓓ 375 bottles

❹ How many more bottles were sold in July than in May?

Ⓕ 150 bottles Ⓗ 125 bottles

Ⓖ 175 bottles Ⓙ 575 bottles

Name _____

This chart shows what 200 fifth-graders chose as their favorite activity during the summer.

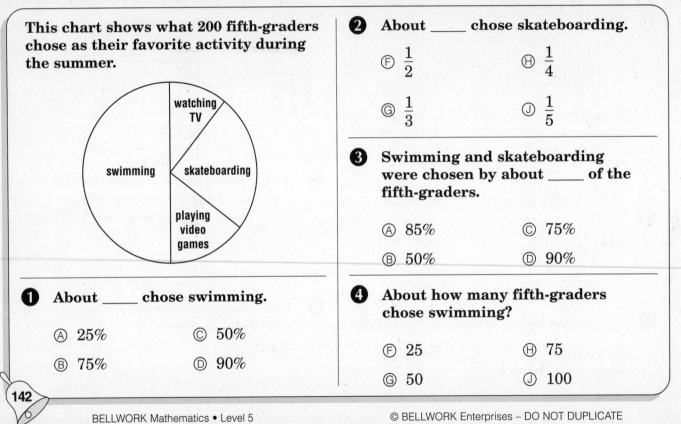

❶ About _____ chose swimming.

Ⓐ 25%   Ⓒ 50%

Ⓑ 75%   Ⓓ 90%

❷ About _____ chose skateboarding.

Ⓕ $\frac{1}{2}$ Ⓗ $\frac{1}{4}$

Ⓖ $\frac{1}{3}$ Ⓙ $\frac{1}{5}$

❸ Swimming and skateboarding were chosen by about _____ of the fifth-graders.

Ⓐ 85%   Ⓒ 75%

Ⓑ 50%   Ⓓ 90%

❹ About how many fifth-graders chose swimming?

Ⓕ 25   Ⓗ 75

Ⓖ 50   Ⓙ 100

❶

$$15 + (-7) =$$

(A) 22   (C) 8

(B) −8   (D) −22

❷

$$1{,}378 \div 26 =$$

(F) 53

(G) 52

(H) 413

(J) 52 R18

❸ Which sign belongs in the ◯ below?

$$\frac{1}{2} \quad \bigcirc \quad \frac{1}{3}$$

(A) >   (B) =   (C) <

❹ Jeff, Sam, Lori, and Sal want to choose teams for volleyball based on height. Sam is 2 inches taller than Jeff. Lori is 1 inch shorter than Sal but 1 inch taller than Jeff. Which of the following statements is not true?

(F) Lori is shorter than Sam.

(G) Sam is taller than Jeff, Lori, and Sal.

(H) Jeff is the shortest.

(J) Sal and Sam are the same height.

143

❶ **What is the area of the figure below?**

2 in.

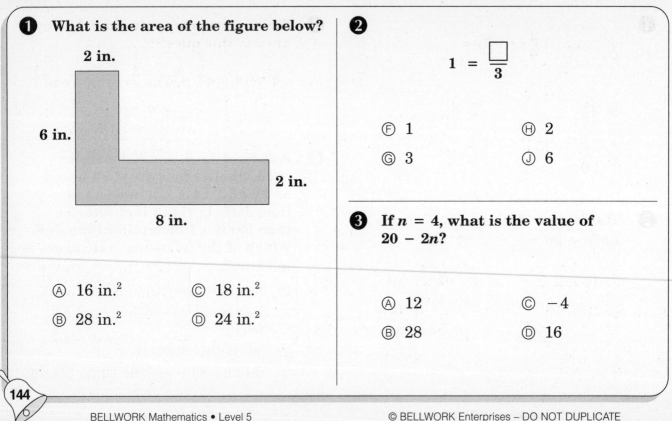

6 in.

2 in.

8 in.

Ⓐ 16 in.²   Ⓒ 18 in.²

Ⓑ 28 in.²   Ⓓ 24 in.²

❷

$$1 = \frac{\square}{3}$$

Ⓕ 1   Ⓗ 2

Ⓖ 3   Ⓙ 6

❸ **If $n = 4$, what is the value of $20 - 2n$?**

Ⓐ 12   Ⓒ −4

Ⓑ 28   Ⓓ 16

Name _____

❶

$$\frac{2}{4} \cdot \frac{3}{5} =$$

Ⓐ $\frac{3}{10}$ Ⓒ $\frac{10}{12}$

Ⓑ $\frac{5}{20}$ Ⓓ $\frac{5}{9}$

❷ The factors (divisors) of 10 are:

Ⓕ 0, 1, 2, 5 Ⓗ 10, 20, 30

Ⓖ 2, 5, 10 Ⓙ 1, 2, 5, 10

❸ Use a centimeter ruler to help answer this question.

Which figure has an area of 8 cm² ?

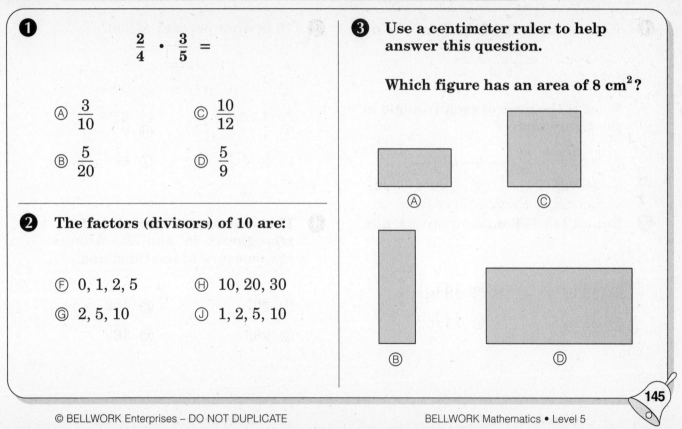

Name _____

1

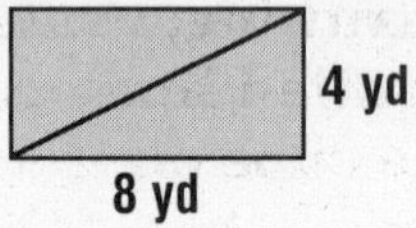

4 yd

8 yd

What is the area of <u>each</u> triangle in the figure above?

Ⓐ 32 yd^2　　Ⓒ 12 yd^2

Ⓑ 16 yd^2　　Ⓓ 6 yd^2

2 **Round 143.958 to the nearest tenth.**

Ⓕ 143.9　　Ⓗ 143.1

Ⓖ 144.0　　Ⓙ 140.0

3 **70 is what percent of 200?**

Ⓐ 7%　　Ⓒ 35%

Ⓑ 14%　　Ⓓ 65%

4 **The measures of two angles of a triangle are 56° and 75°. What is the measure of the third angle?**

Ⓕ 90°　　Ⓗ 180°

Ⓖ 49°　　Ⓙ 229°

Name _____

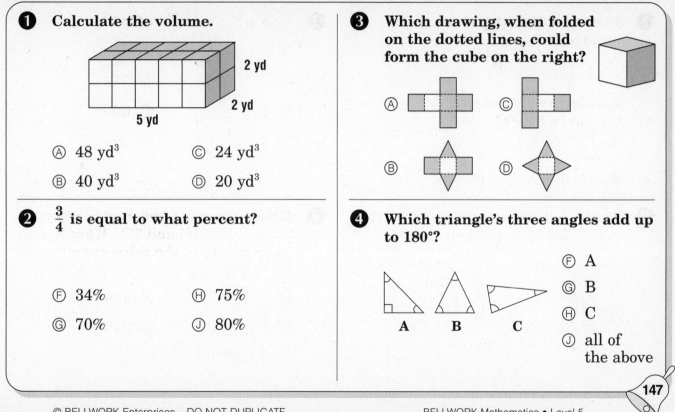

1 Calculate the volume.

2 yd
2 yd
5 yd

Ⓐ 48 yd³   Ⓒ 24 yd³

Ⓑ 40 yd³   Ⓓ 20 yd³

2 $\frac{3}{4}$ is equal to what percent?

Ⓕ 34%   Ⓗ 75%

Ⓖ 70%   Ⓙ 80%

3 Which drawing, when folded on the dotted lines, could form the cube on the right?

Ⓐ   Ⓒ

Ⓑ   Ⓓ

4 Which triangle's three angles add up to 180°?

A   B   C

Ⓕ A

Ⓖ B

Ⓗ C

Ⓙ all of the above

BELLWORK Mathematics • Level 5

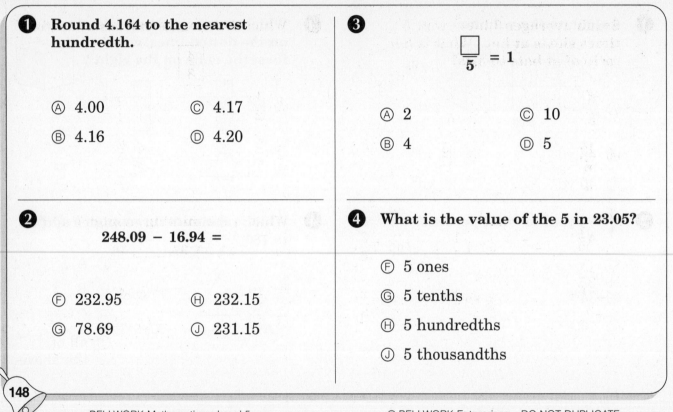

Name _____

❶ Round 4.164 to the nearest hundredth.

Ⓐ 4.00   Ⓒ 4.17

Ⓑ 4.16   Ⓓ 4.20

❷
$$248.09 - 16.94 =$$

Ⓕ 232.95   Ⓗ 232.15

Ⓖ 78.69   Ⓙ 231.15

❸
$$\frac{\square}{5} = 1$$

Ⓐ 2   Ⓒ 10

Ⓑ 4   Ⓓ 5

❹ What is the value of the 5 in 23.05?

Ⓕ 5 ones

Ⓖ 5 tenths

Ⓗ 5 hundredths

Ⓙ 5 thousandths

148

Name _____

1 Sarah averages 3 hits every 5 times she is at bat. What is her ratio of at bats to hits?

Ⓐ $\frac{5}{3}$　　Ⓒ $\frac{3}{5}$

Ⓑ $\frac{15}{5}$　　Ⓓ $\frac{5}{15}$

2
$$4\frac{2}{6}$$
$$+\ 3\frac{2}{6}$$

Ⓕ $7\frac{1}{2}$　　Ⓗ $7\frac{3}{6}$

Ⓖ $7\frac{1}{3}$　　Ⓙ $7\frac{2}{3}$

3 Which fraction is another name for:

$$\boxed{\frac{4}{8}}$$

Ⓐ $\frac{1}{2}$　　Ⓒ $\frac{8}{4}$

Ⓑ $\frac{1}{4}$　　Ⓓ $\frac{2}{8}$

4 What is the missing number?

24, 30, 36, ____, 48

Ⓕ 42　　Ⓗ 44

Ⓖ 40　　Ⓙ 46

1 What is the prime factorization of 50?

Ⓐ $2 \times 2 \times 5$

Ⓑ $2 \times 5 \times 5 \times 5$

Ⓒ 2×5^2

Ⓓ $2^2 \times 5^2$

2 Ben added $\frac{1}{2}$ cup of flour to the cookie dough. He then added another $\frac{1}{3}$ cup of flour. How much flour did Ben add to the cookie dough?

Ⓕ $\frac{2}{6}$ cup

Ⓖ $\frac{2}{5}$ cup

Ⓗ $\frac{5}{6}$ cup

Ⓙ $\frac{1}{6}$ cup

3
$$\frac{\square}{2} = 1$$

Ⓐ 1

Ⓑ 2

Ⓒ 3

Ⓓ 4

4 Use the associative property to answer the problem below.

$$4 \times (7 \times 6) = (4 \times \square) \times 6$$

Ⓕ 13

Ⓖ 7

Ⓗ 28

Ⓙ 10

150

Name _____

❶

$$3\frac{2}{3}$$

$$-\ 1\frac{1}{3}$$

Ⓐ $2\frac{1}{3}$　　Ⓒ 5

Ⓑ $1\frac{2}{3}$　　Ⓓ 2

❷

234.16

+ 185.48

Ⓕ 319.54

Ⓖ 151.32

Ⓗ 419.91

Ⓙ 419.64

Ⓚ none of these

❸ An orange is an example of which space figure?

Ⓐ cylinder　　Ⓒ circle

Ⓑ cone　　Ⓓ sphere

❹ Colin bought 3 pounds of oranges for 20¢ a pound. How much change should he receive from a dollar?

Ⓕ 60¢　　Ⓗ 20¢

Ⓖ 80¢　　Ⓙ 40¢

151

Name _____

1 **Use the distributive property to simplify the expression below.**

$$4(x + 3)$$

Ⓐ $4 + x + 12$ Ⓒ $4x + 3$

Ⓑ $4x + 12$ Ⓓ $x + 12$

2 **Which of these is equal to 100?**

Ⓕ 2^{10} Ⓗ 10^{10}

Ⓖ 10^2 Ⓙ 5^4

3 **Find the mean (average), median, and mode of the following numbers:**

$$(2, 2, 3, 5, 8)$$

mean: _____ mode: _____

median: _____

4 **Find the volume.**

Ⓐ 12 ft^3

Ⓑ 64 ft^3

Ⓒ 96 ft^3

Ⓓ 16 ft^3

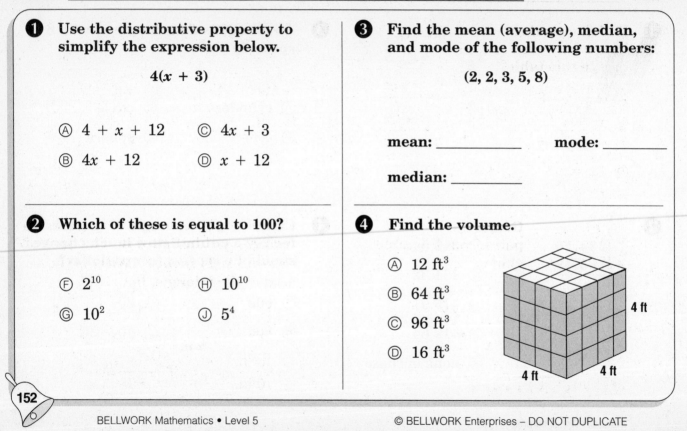

4 ft

4 ft 4 ft

Name _____

① **Which equation below was used to create this table?**

x	y
1	3
2	6
3	9
4	12

Ⓐ $x = y + 3$

Ⓑ $x = y$

Ⓒ $y = x + 2$

Ⓓ $3x = y$

③ **What is 35% of 400?**

Ⓕ 140

Ⓖ 70

Ⓗ 105

Ⓙ 11.4

② **Graph the ordered pairs from the table above.**

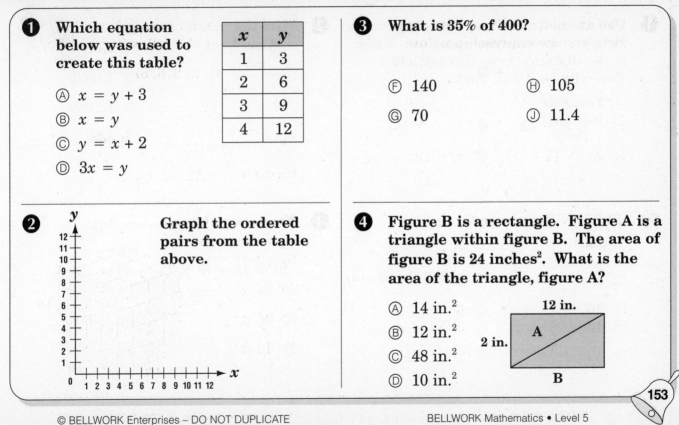

④ **Figure B is a rectangle. Figure A is a triangle within figure B. The area of figure B is 24 inches². What is the area of the triangle, figure A?**

Ⓐ 14 in.²

Ⓑ 12 in.²

Ⓒ 48 in.²

Ⓓ 10 in.²

BELLWORK Mathematics • Level 5

Name _____

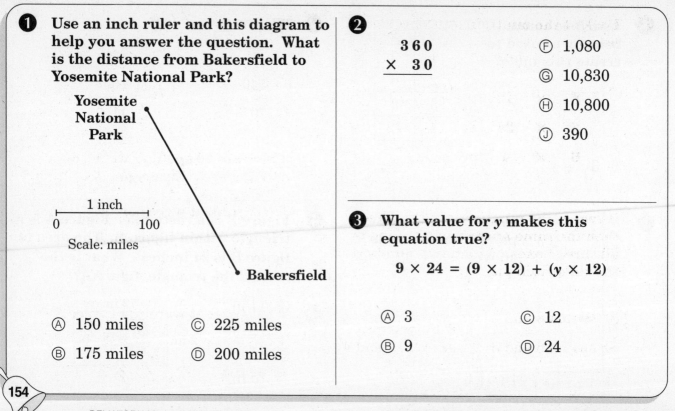

1 Use an inch ruler and this diagram to help you answer the question. What is the distance from Bakersfield to Yosemite National Park?

Yosemite
National
Park

1 inch
0   100
Scale: miles

Bakersfield

Ⓐ 150 miles   Ⓒ 225 miles

Ⓑ 175 miles   Ⓓ 200 miles

2

$$360$$
$$\times\ \ 30$$

Ⓕ 1,080

Ⓖ 10,830

Ⓗ 10,800

Ⓙ 390

3 What value for *y* makes this equation true?

$$9 \times 24 = (9 \times 12) + (y \times 12)$$

Ⓐ 3   Ⓒ 12

Ⓑ 9   Ⓓ 24

❶ **Look at the multiplication problems below.**

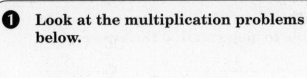

$$8 \times 12 = \square$$
$$2 \times 24 = \square$$
$$6 \times 4 = \square$$

If two of the numbers are switched, then the same answer will belong in all three boxes. Which two numbers should switch places?

Ⓐ switch 8 and 4   Ⓒ switch 2 and 4

Ⓑ switch 6 and 8   Ⓓ switch 12 and 4

❷

$$\frac{4}{6}$$
$$-\frac{2}{6}$$

Ⓕ $\frac{1}{2}$ Ⓗ $\frac{1}{6}$

Ⓖ $\frac{1}{3}$ Ⓙ 1

There are 20 spelling words on a spelling test. Karen got 15 correct.

❸ **What percent were correct?**

Ⓐ 25%   Ⓒ 70%

Ⓑ 75%   Ⓓ 7.5%

❹ **What percent were not correct?**

Ⓕ 75%   Ⓗ 25%

Ⓖ 92.5%   Ⓙ 30%

155

1 A new ruler exactly balances 15 pencils on a scale. How many pencils would you need to balance 7 rulers? Use the table to help you find the answer.

Pencils	15	30						
Rulers	1	2	3					

Ⓐ 2 pencils   ©️ 120 pencils

Ⓑ 100 pencils   Ⓓ 105 pencils

2 Katie and her father caught 18 fish. They gave $\frac{1}{3}$ of the fish away to friends. How many fish did they keep for themselves?

Ⓕ 6 fish   Ⓗ 10 fish

Ⓖ 8 fish   Ⓙ 12 fish

3 There are seven bananas on the ground. Two monkeys eat all of the bananas. Each monkey eats at least one. List all of the combinations the two monkeys could have eaten.

Name _____

 1 **A spinner was spun 200 times. The results are shown in the table below.**

	W	X	Y	Z
Number of times the spinner landed on a letter.	20	80	80	20

Which spinner was most likely used?

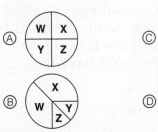

Ⓐ Ⓑ Ⓒ Ⓓ

2 **Using each of the numerals 3, 6, 7, and 8 one time only, what is the largest number you can make:**

with 8 in the ones place? _____

with 8 in the tens place? _____

with 8 in the hundreds place? _____

with 8 in the thousands place? _____

3 **Using the numbers you wrote, find the difference between the number of greatest value and the number of least value.**

_____

BELLWORK Mathematics • Level 5

1

$$4^2 + 2^3 =$$

Ⓐ 20   Ⓒ 16

Ⓑ 32   Ⓓ 24

2 What is the value of *z*? Solve using the distributive property.

$$2(z - 4) = 4$$

Ⓕ 4   Ⓗ 5

Ⓖ 6   Ⓙ 3

3 What is the estimated answer?

$ 63.15
    3.98
+ 2.75

Ⓐ $75.00

Ⓑ $65.00

Ⓒ $71.00

Ⓓ $70.00

Ⓔ none of the above

4 What is the volume?

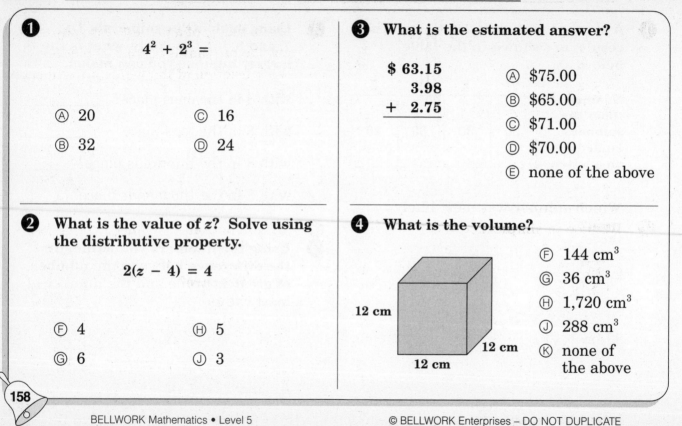

12 cm

12 cm

12 cm

Ⓕ 144 cm³

Ⓖ 36 cm³

Ⓗ 1,720 cm³

Ⓙ 288 cm³

Ⓚ none of the above

Name _____

❶

$$2\ \frac{1}{5}$$

$$+\ 3\ \frac{2}{10}$$

Ⓐ $\frac{2}{5}$ Ⓒ $5\ \frac{3}{10}$

Ⓑ $5\ \frac{2}{5}$ Ⓓ $5\ \frac{3}{15}$

❸ Maria has $\frac{1}{2}$ of a pie left. She needs to cut the pie that is left into 6 pieces. What fraction of the whole pie will each piece be?

Ⓐ $\frac{1}{2} \times \frac{1}{6} = \frac{1}{12}$ Ⓒ $\frac{1}{2} \div \frac{1}{6} = 3$

Ⓑ $\frac{1}{2} + \frac{1}{6} = \frac{2}{3}$ Ⓓ $\frac{1}{2} - \frac{1}{6} = \frac{1}{3}$

❷ **Reduce to simplest terms.**

$$\boxed{\frac{20}{3}}$$

Ⓕ $6\ \frac{2}{3}$ Ⓗ $6\ \frac{1}{3}$

Ⓖ $7\ \frac{1}{3}$ Ⓙ 7

❹ **What fraction of students like mysteries as their favorite genre?**

FAVORITE GENRE

Mystery 20%
Suspense 15%
Comedy 50%
Non-fiction 15%

Ⓕ $\frac{1}{4}$ Ⓗ $\frac{1}{20}$

Ⓖ $\frac{1}{5}$ Ⓙ $\frac{1}{6}$

159

Name _____

1

$5\frac{3}{4}$

$-1\frac{1}{4}$

Ⓐ $4\frac{1}{4}$ Ⓒ $4\frac{1}{2}$

Ⓑ 7 Ⓓ $3\frac{1}{2}$

3 Anna had a board that was 10 feet long. She cut off 3 pieces that were each 3 feet long. How much of the board was left?

Ⓐ 4 feet   Ⓒ 9 feet

Ⓑ 16 feet   Ⓓ 1 foot

2

$33,469$
$-21,579$

Ⓕ 11,880

Ⓖ 12,110

Ⓗ 55,048

Ⓙ 11,890

Ⓚ none of these

4 Donna went to a farm and picked peaches, plums, and oranges. Of the fruit she picked, $\frac{1}{6}$ were peaches and $\frac{3}{6}$ were plums. What fraction of the fruit were peaches or plums?

Ⓕ $\frac{1}{3}$ Ⓗ $\frac{2}{3}$

Ⓖ $\frac{1}{2}$ Ⓙ $\frac{8}{6}$

1

$$0.6 \times 0.5 =$$

Ⓐ 3.0   Ⓒ 0.03

Ⓑ 0.3   Ⓓ 30

2

$$400 \div 0.25 =$$

Ⓕ 0.16   Ⓗ 160

Ⓖ 16   Ⓙ 1,600

3

$5\frac{2}{10}$ Ⓐ $7\frac{2}{5}$ Ⓒ $7\frac{4}{20}$

$+ \ 2\frac{2}{10}$ Ⓑ $\frac{4}{10}$ Ⓓ $7\frac{4}{5}$

4 **The number 18 is divisible by:**

Ⓕ 2, 3, 5   Ⓗ 2, 3, 4

Ⓖ 2, 3, 8   Ⓙ 2, 3, 6

161

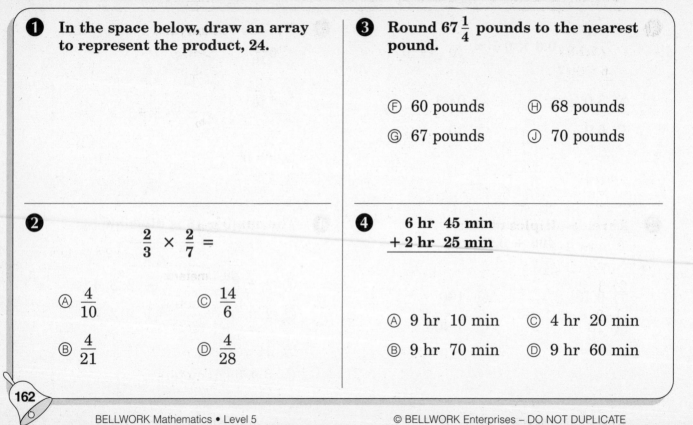

Name _____

1 In the space below, draw an array to represent the product, 24.

2

$$\frac{2}{3} \times \frac{2}{7} =$$

(A) $\frac{4}{10}$ (C) $\frac{14}{6}$

(B) $\frac{4}{21}$ (D) $\frac{4}{28}$

3 Round $67\frac{1}{4}$ pounds to the nearest pound.

(F) 60 pounds   (H) 68 pounds

(G) 67 pounds   (J) 70 pounds

4
```
   6 hr  45 min
+ 2 hr  25 min
```

(A) 9 hr 10 min   (C) 4 hr 20 min

(B) 9 hr 70 min   (D) 9 hr 60 min

162

Name _____

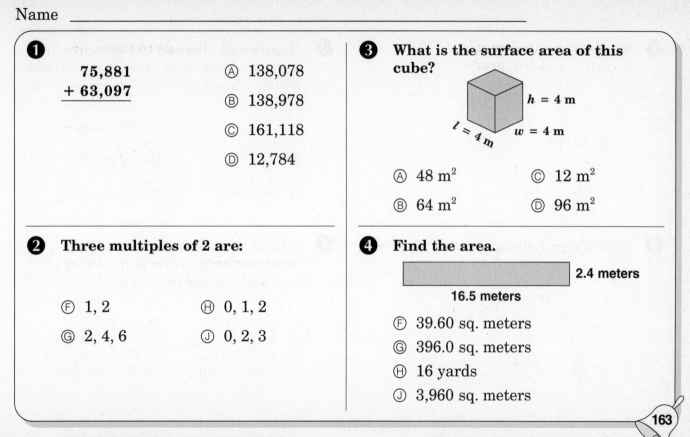

❶

$$\begin{array}{r} 75{,}881 \\ +\ 63{,}097 \\ \hline \end{array}$$

ⓐ 138,078

ⓑ 138,978

ⓒ 161,118

ⓓ 12,784

❷ Three multiples of 2 are:

ⓕ 1, 2   ⓗ 0, 1, 2

ⓖ 2, 4, 6   ⓙ 0, 2, 3

❸ What is the surface area of this cube?

$h = 4$ m

$l = 4$ m $w = 4$ m

ⓐ 48 m^2 ⓒ 12 m^2

ⓑ 64 m^2 ⓓ 96 m^2

❹ Find the area.

2.4 meters

16.5 meters

ⓕ 39.60 sq. meters

ⓖ 396.0 sq. meters

ⓗ 16 yards

ⓙ 3,960 sq. meters

1 **Three multiples of 5 are:**

Ⓐ 1, 5, 10   Ⓒ 0, 10, 20

Ⓑ 5, 10, 15   Ⓓ 0, 1, 5

3 **A car wash cleaned 120 cars in one day. Of those cars, 40% were painted white. How many cars were painted white?**

Ⓐ 30 cars   Ⓒ 50 cars

Ⓑ 48 cars   Ⓓ 60 cars

2 **Which sign belongs in the ◯ below?**

$$\frac{3}{8} \quad \bigcirc \quad \frac{1}{4}$$

Ⓕ >   Ⓖ =   Ⓗ <

4 **A farm produces 60 bales of hay from one acre. How many bales of hay will 5 acres produce?**

Ⓕ 300 bales   Ⓗ 12 bales

Ⓖ 100 bales   Ⓙ 30 bales

Name _____

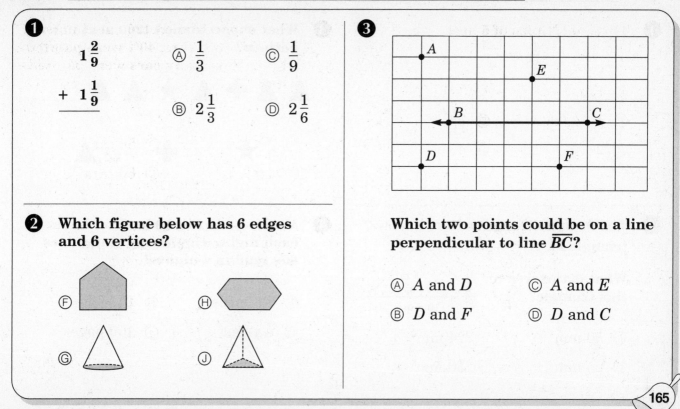

1

$$1\frac{2}{9}$$
$$+\ 1\frac{1}{9}$$
____

Ⓐ $\frac{1}{3}$ Ⓒ $\frac{1}{9}$

Ⓑ $2\frac{1}{3}$ Ⓓ $2\frac{1}{6}$

2 **Which figure below has 6 edges and 6 vertices?**

Ⓕ

Ⓗ

Ⓖ

Ⓙ

3

Which two points could be on a line perpendicular to line $\overline{BC}$?

Ⓐ A and D Ⓒ A and E

Ⓑ D and F Ⓓ D and C

165

Name _____

1

$$\frac{1}{2} = \frac{\square}{4}$$

Ⓐ 1   Ⓒ 3

Ⓑ 2   Ⓓ 4

2 The formula for the area of a triangle is: $A = \frac{b \times h}{2}$.

What is the area of this triangle?

5 mm

10 mm

Ⓕ 50 mm²   Ⓗ 24 mm²

Ⓖ 25 mm²   Ⓙ 30 mm²

3 What shape would come next in the pattern?

▲ ▲ ✚ ▲ ★ ▲ ▲ ____

Ⓐ ★   Ⓑ ✚   Ⓒ ▲

4 Maria reads 20 pages of her book each night. How many pages does she read in 4 nights?

Ⓕ 80 pages   Ⓗ 24 pages

Ⓖ 5 pages   Ⓙ 100 pages

166

Name _____

1

$$510 \times 20$$

Ⓐ 10,730

Ⓑ 10,200

Ⓒ 10,100

Ⓓ 1,540

2

$$5 \text{ hr } 10 \text{ min} - 1 \text{ hr } 20 \text{ min}$$

Ⓕ 3 hr 50 min   Ⓗ 4 hr 0 min

Ⓖ 6 hr 20 min   Ⓙ 6 hr 90 min

3 Use the commutative property to answer the problem below.

$$5 \times \square = 7 \times 5$$

Ⓐ 12   Ⓒ 35

Ⓑ 7   Ⓓ 17

4

$$\frac{2}{3} = \frac{\square}{6}$$

Ⓕ 3   Ⓗ 5

Ⓖ 2   Ⓙ 4

Name _____

❶ **Which number is five thousand, four?**

Ⓐ 5,400 Ⓒ 5,004

Ⓑ 5,040 Ⓓ 5,044

❷

$$\frac{2}{6} + \frac{1}{6} =$$

Ⓕ $\frac{3}{12}$ Ⓗ $\frac{1}{2}$

Ⓖ $\frac{1}{4}$ Ⓙ $\frac{1}{3}$

❸ **Three multiples of 6 are:**

Ⓐ 1, 3, 6 Ⓒ 0, 1, 6

Ⓑ 6, 12, 18 Ⓓ 1, 6, 10

❹ **In the table below, the rule is:**

IN	OUT
15	3
20	4
25	5
30	6

Ⓕ subtract 12

Ⓖ divide by 5

Ⓗ multiply by 5

Ⓙ add 16

Name _____

1 **Which fraction is another name for:**

$$\frac{3}{5}$$

Ⓐ $\frac{3}{10}$　　　Ⓒ $\frac{6}{10}$

Ⓑ $\frac{6}{5}$　　　Ⓓ $\frac{5}{3}$

2

$$3\frac{1}{3}$$
$$+ \ 2\frac{2}{3}$$

Ⓕ $5\frac{2}{3}$　　Ⓗ 6

Ⓖ $5\frac{1}{3}$　　Ⓙ $\frac{2}{3}$

3 **If $m = 16.47$, what is the value of $20 - m$?**

Ⓐ 36.47　　　Ⓒ 16.47

Ⓑ 4.63　　　Ⓓ 3.53

4 **What is the value of the 8 in 10.86?**

Ⓕ 8 ones

Ⓖ 8 tens

Ⓗ 8 hundredths

Ⓙ 8 tenths

169

❶

$$\begin{array}{r} 95{,}061 \\ +\ 37{,}783 \\ \hline \end{array}$$

Ⓐ 132,044

Ⓑ 161,114

Ⓒ 57,278

Ⓓ 132,844

❷ Hannah was born in 1995. Luke was born in 1999. Who is older?

Ⓕ Hannah

Ⓖ Luke

❸

$$\begin{array}{r} 3\frac{5}{8} \\ +\ \frac{2}{8} \\ \hline \end{array}$$

Ⓐ $3\frac{7}{8}$ Ⓒ $3\frac{3}{8}$

Ⓑ 4   Ⓓ $3\frac{3}{4}$

❹

$$\frac{3}{5} = \frac{\square}{15}$$

Ⓕ 15   Ⓗ 9

Ⓖ 6   Ⓙ 10

Name _____

1

$$\frac{1}{2}$$
$$+ \ \frac{1}{4}$$

(A) 1   (C) $\frac{1}{4}$

(B) $\frac{3}{4}$ (D) $1\frac{1}{4}$

2

$$10\frac{8}{9}$$
$$- \ 7\frac{2}{9}$$

(F) $3\frac{2}{3}$ (H) $18\frac{1}{9}$

(G) $3\frac{5}{9}$ (J) $3\frac{3}{4}$

3 What is the sum of the angles of this quadrilateral?

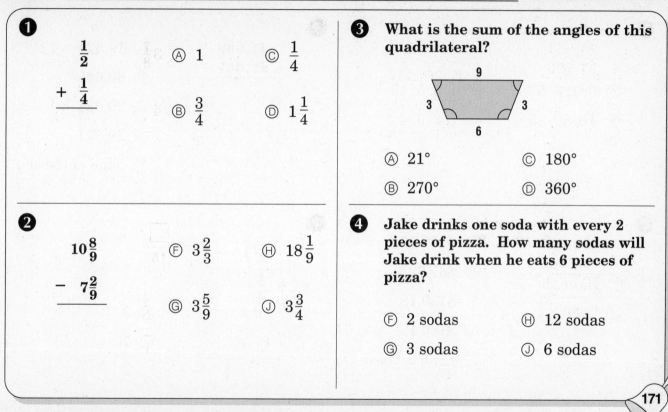

(A) 21°   (C) 180°

(B) 270°   (D) 360°

4 Jake drinks one soda with every 2 pieces of pizza. How many sodas will Jake drink when he eats 6 pieces of pizza?

(F) 2 sodas   (H) 12 sodas

(G) 3 sodas   (J) 6 sodas

171

Name _____

❶ **The factors (divisors) of 15 are:**

Ⓐ 0, 1, 3, 5   Ⓒ 1, 3, 5, 15

Ⓑ 15, 30, 45   Ⓓ 1, 2, 3, 4

❷

$$\begin{array}{r} \$\ \ 94.00 \\ +\ \ 56.18 \\ \hline \end{array}$$

Ⓕ $150.00

Ⓖ $37.82

Ⓗ $150.18

Ⓙ $140.18

Ⓚ none of these

❸

$$\begin{array}{r} 41{,}008 \\ -\ 21{,}637 \\ \hline \end{array}$$

Ⓐ 19,371

Ⓑ 62,645

Ⓒ 20,631

Ⓓ 29,371

Ⓔ none of these

❹

$$\begin{array}{r} \dfrac{1}{2} \\ +\ \dfrac{1}{3} \\ \hline \end{array}$$

Ⓕ $\dfrac{2}{5}$ Ⓗ $\dfrac{5}{6}$

Ⓖ $\dfrac{4}{6}$ Ⓙ $\dfrac{1}{2}$

Name _____

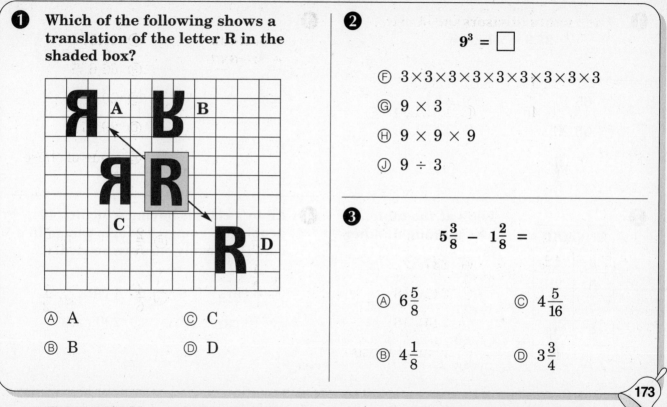

❶ **Which of the following shows a translation of the letter R in the shaded box?**

Ⓐ A

Ⓑ B

Ⓒ C

Ⓓ D

❷ $9^3 = \square$

Ⓕ $3 \times 3 \times 3 \times 3 \times 3 \times 3 \times 3 \times 3 \times 3$

Ⓖ 9×3

Ⓗ $9 \times 9 \times 9$

Ⓙ $9 \div 3$

❸ $5\frac{3}{8} - 1\frac{2}{8} =$

Ⓐ $6\frac{5}{8}$

Ⓒ $4\frac{5}{16}$

Ⓑ $4\frac{1}{8}$

Ⓓ $3\frac{3}{4}$

①

$$23.9 + 41.20 =$$

Ⓐ 65.1   Ⓒ 64.1

Ⓑ 65.29   Ⓓ 43.59

③

$$\begin{array}{r} \frac{3}{4} \\ -\frac{1}{2} \\ \hline \end{array}$$

Ⓐ 1   Ⓒ $1\frac{1}{4}$

Ⓑ $\frac{1}{4}$ Ⓓ $\frac{2}{3}$

②

IN	OUT
3	12
5	20
7	
9	36

Look at the table. The missing number is ____.

Ⓕ 9

Ⓖ 21

Ⓗ 28

Ⓙ 35

④ Libby's class is having a picnic. 40 people are going. 5 people can go in a car. How many cars are needed?

Ⓕ 8 cars   Ⓗ 4 cars

Ⓖ 10 cars   Ⓙ 200 cars

1 Three multiples of 10 are:

Ⓐ 1, 5, 10   Ⓒ 10, 20, 30

Ⓑ 0, 5, 10   Ⓓ 5, 10, 15

3

$$1.1 \times 0.3 =$$

Ⓐ 3.3   Ⓒ 0.303

Ⓑ 0.33   Ⓓ 0.033

2 Toni and her 2 sisters went to the movies. The tickets cost $5.75 per person. Also, they spent $4.50 each for popcorn and drinks. How much did the three girls spend altogether?

Ⓕ $13.50   Ⓗ $17.25

Ⓖ $30.25   Ⓙ $30.75

4 Round $24\frac{7}{8}$ inches to the nearest inch.

Ⓕ 24 inches   Ⓗ 25 inches

Ⓖ 23 inches   Ⓙ 26 inches

175

1 On one spin of the spinner, the probability it will stop on A is:

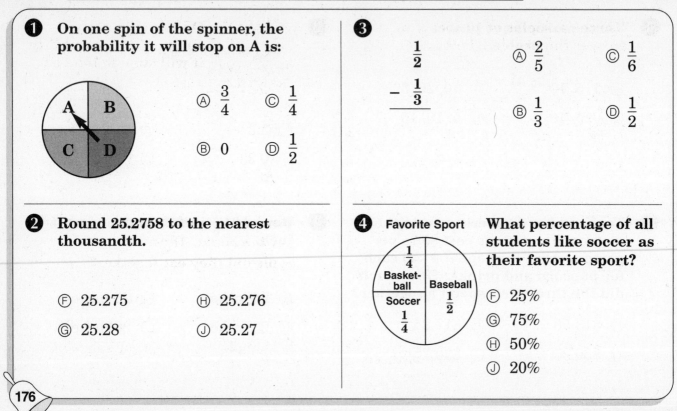

Ⓐ $\frac{3}{4}$　　Ⓒ $\frac{1}{4}$

Ⓑ 0　　Ⓓ $\frac{1}{2}$

2 Round 25.2758 to the nearest thousandth.

Ⓕ 25.275　　Ⓗ 25.276

Ⓖ 25.28　　Ⓙ 25.27

3

$\frac{1}{2}$
$-\frac{1}{3}$

Ⓐ $\frac{2}{5}$　　Ⓒ $\frac{1}{6}$

Ⓑ $\frac{1}{3}$　　Ⓓ $\frac{1}{2}$

4 Favorite Sport

What percentage of all students like soccer as their favorite sport?

$\frac{1}{4}$ Basketball
Soccer $\frac{1}{4}$
Baseball $\frac{1}{2}$

Ⓕ 25%

Ⓖ 75%

Ⓗ 50%

Ⓙ 20%

Name _____

❶ Use the associative property to answer the problem below.

$$9 \times (\square \times 4) = (9 \times 7) \times 4$$

Ⓐ 63 Ⓒ 36

Ⓑ 9 Ⓓ 7

❷

$$\begin{array}{r} 51{,}120 \\ -\ 46{,}231 \\ \hline \end{array}$$

Ⓕ 97,351

Ⓖ 4,889

Ⓗ 15,111

Ⓙ 15,999

Ⓚ none of these

❸ 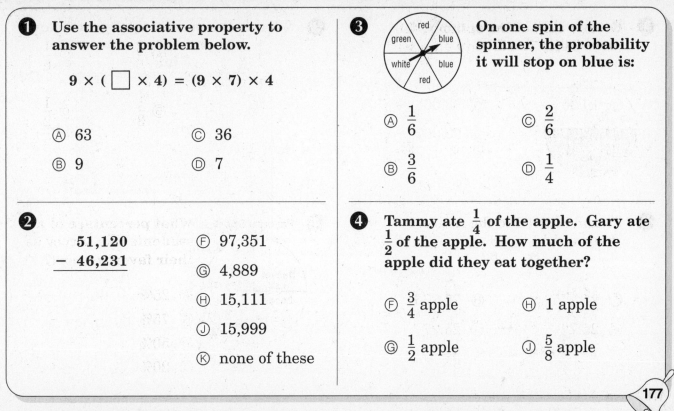 On one spin of the spinner, the probability it will stop on blue is:

Ⓐ $\dfrac{1}{6}$ Ⓒ $\dfrac{2}{6}$

Ⓑ $\dfrac{3}{6}$ Ⓓ $\dfrac{1}{4}$

❹ Tammy ate $\dfrac{1}{4}$ of the apple. Gary ate $\dfrac{1}{2}$ of the apple. How much of the apple did they eat together?

Ⓕ $\dfrac{3}{4}$ apple Ⓗ 1 apple

Ⓖ $\dfrac{1}{2}$ apple Ⓙ $\dfrac{5}{8}$ apple

❶ Round 93.0674 to the nearest hundredth.

Ⓐ 10.00 Ⓒ 93.06

Ⓑ 93.07 Ⓓ 93.067

❷

$$\frac{5}{8} - \frac{3}{8} =$$

Ⓕ $\frac{1}{4}$ Ⓗ $\frac{2}{0}$

Ⓖ 1 Ⓙ $\frac{1}{8}$

❸ What is the area of the figure below?

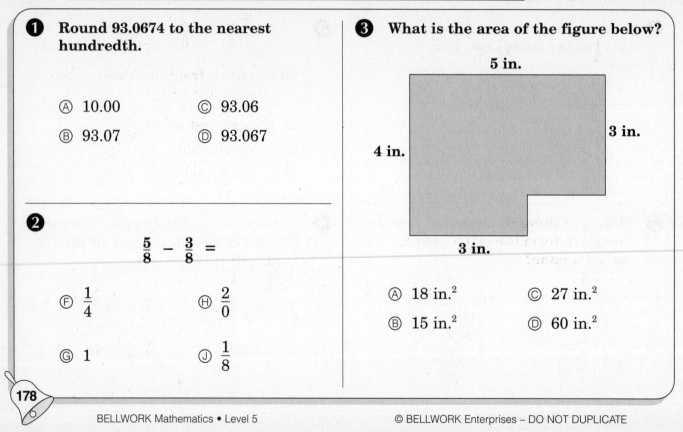

5 in.

3 in.

4 in.

3 in.

Ⓐ 18 in.² Ⓒ 27 in.²

Ⓑ 15 in.² Ⓓ 60 in.²

❶

$$\frac{1}{3}$$

$$+ \ \frac{1}{5}$$

Ⓐ $\frac{8}{15}$

Ⓒ $\frac{2}{15}$

Ⓑ $\frac{1}{4}$

Ⓓ $\frac{1}{8}$

❸

$$\frac{3}{5} \qquad \frac{3}{8} \qquad \boxed{\frac{3}{4}}$$

Of the three fractions shown above, the one that is circled has —

Ⓐ the greatest value.

Ⓑ the least value.

Ⓒ the same value.

❷ Which of these flat shapes could be folded to form the space figure called a cube?

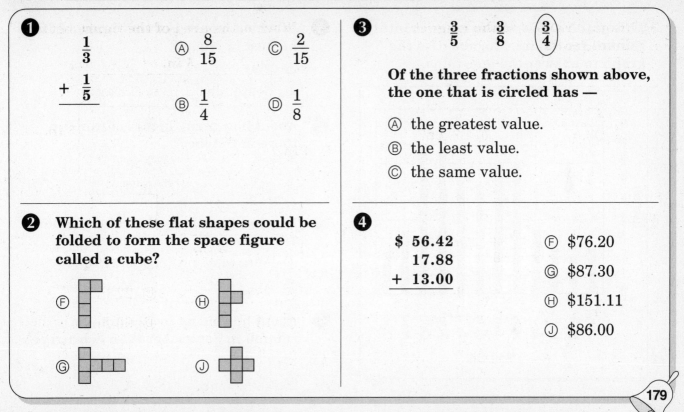

Ⓕ

Ⓗ

Ⓖ

Ⓙ

❹

$$\begin{array}{r} \$ \ 56.42 \\ 17.88 \\ + \ 13.00 \\ \hline \end{array}$$

Ⓕ $76.20

Ⓖ $87.30

Ⓗ $151.11

Ⓙ $86.00

179

Name _____

This graph shows the average monthly rainfall for Miami, Florida. Use the graph to answer the questions.

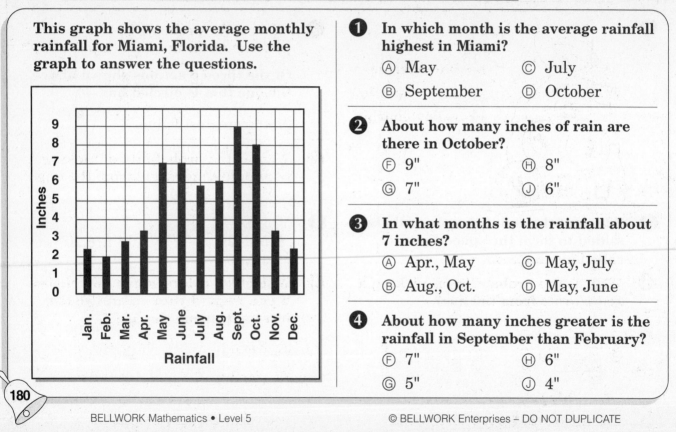

Inches

Rainfall

① In which month is the average rainfall highest in Miami?
Ⓐ May   Ⓒ July
Ⓑ September   Ⓓ October

② About how many inches of rain are there in October?
Ⓕ 9"   Ⓗ 8"
Ⓖ 7"   Ⓙ 6"

③ In what months is the rainfall about 7 inches?
Ⓐ Apr., May   Ⓒ May, July
Ⓑ Aug., Oct.   Ⓓ May, June

④ About how many inches greater is the rainfall in September than February?
Ⓕ 7"   Ⓗ 6"
Ⓖ 5"   Ⓙ 4"

180

Name _____

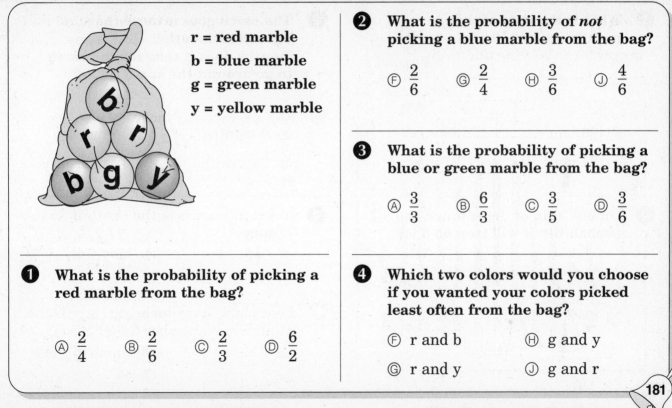

r = red marble
b = blue marble
g = green marble
y = yellow marble

❷ What is the probability of *not* picking a blue marble from the bag?

Ⓕ $\frac{2}{6}$ Ⓖ $\frac{2}{4}$ Ⓗ $\frac{3}{6}$ Ⓙ $\frac{4}{6}$

❸ What is the probability of picking a blue or green marble from the bag?

Ⓐ $\frac{3}{3}$ Ⓑ $\frac{6}{3}$ Ⓒ $\frac{3}{5}$ Ⓓ $\frac{3}{6}$

❶ What is the probability of picking a red marble from the bag?

Ⓐ $\frac{2}{4}$ Ⓑ $\frac{2}{6}$ Ⓒ $\frac{2}{3}$ Ⓓ $\frac{6}{2}$

❹ Which two colors would you choose if you wanted your colors picked least often from the bag?

Ⓕ r and b Ⓗ g and y

Ⓖ r and y Ⓙ g and r

181

1 **What is the area of this parallelogram?**

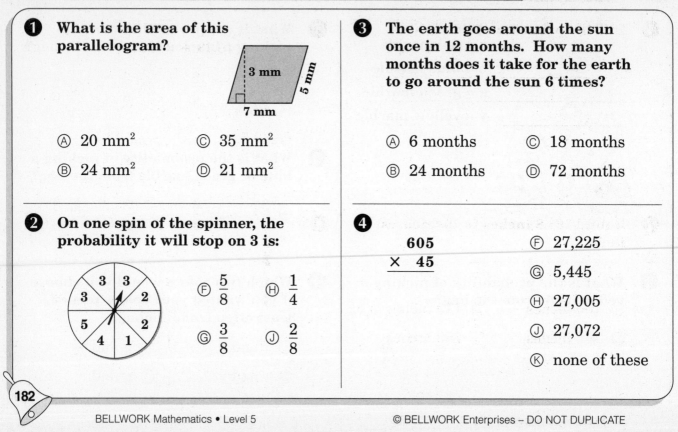

3 mm
5 mm
7 mm

Ⓐ 20 mm² Ⓒ 35 mm²

Ⓑ 24 mm² Ⓓ 21 mm²

2 **On one spin of the spinner, the probability it will stop on 3 is:**

3 3
3 2
5 2
4 1

Ⓕ $\frac{5}{8}$ Ⓗ $\frac{1}{4}$

Ⓖ $\frac{3}{8}$ Ⓙ $\frac{2}{8}$

3 **The earth goes around the sun once in 12 months. How many months does it take for the earth to go around the sun 6 times?**

Ⓐ 6 months Ⓒ 18 months

Ⓑ 24 months Ⓓ 72 months

4

605
× 45

Ⓕ 27,225

Ⓖ 5,445

Ⓗ 27,005

Ⓙ 27,072

Ⓚ none of these

① **List the prime numbers to 50.**

_____

_____

_____

② **Round 163.8 inches to the nearest inch.**

Ⓐ 160 inches Ⓒ 170 inches

Ⓑ 164 inches Ⓓ 163 inches

③

$$16.23 + 24.28 =$$

Ⓕ 40.41 Ⓗ 8.05

Ⓖ 40.51 Ⓙ 30.51

④

$$\frac{1}{2}$$
$$+ \frac{2}{5}$$

Ⓐ $\frac{1}{5}$ Ⓒ $\frac{3}{5}$

Ⓑ $\frac{9}{10}$ Ⓓ $\frac{3}{7}$

183

❶ **Which number is divisible by 4, 5, and 8?**

Ⓐ 30   Ⓒ 50

Ⓑ 40   Ⓓ 60

❷

$$10\overline{)2,000}$$

Ⓕ 200   Ⓗ 2,000

Ⓖ 20   Ⓙ 1,000

❸

$$\frac{1}{2} = \frac{\square}{6}$$

Ⓐ 4   Ⓒ 3

Ⓑ 2   Ⓓ 5

❹ **Which sign belongs in the ◯ below?**

$$80 + 0 \quad \bigcirc \quad 4 \times 15$$

Ⓕ >   Ⓖ =   Ⓗ <

Name _____

❶

$$\frac{2}{3}$$
$$-\frac{1}{2}$$

Ⓐ $\frac{1}{3}$ Ⓒ $\frac{1}{2}$

Ⓑ $\frac{5}{6}$ Ⓓ $\frac{1}{6}$

❸

$$\begin{array}{r} 407 \\ \times\ \ 80 \end{array}$$

Ⓐ 32,560

Ⓑ 32,567

Ⓒ 3,256

Ⓓ 32,650

❷ A class left on a field trip at 1:45 p.m. and returned at 3:30 p.m. How long were they gone?

Ⓕ 2 hr 15 min   Ⓗ 1 hr 15 min

Ⓖ 1 hr 45 min   Ⓙ 2 hr 45 min

❹

$$2\overline{)\$4.26}$$

Ⓕ $2.13

Ⓖ $2.01

Ⓗ $2.31

Ⓙ $2.03

185

Name _____

1 **The prime factorization of 9 is:**

Ⓐ 1, 3, 9   Ⓒ 3 × 2

Ⓑ 3 × 3   Ⓓ 3 × 3 × 3

3 **Three multiples of 9 are:**

Ⓐ 9, 18, 27   Ⓒ 3, 6, 9

Ⓑ 0, 1, 3   Ⓓ 1, 3, 9

2

$$\begin{array}{r} \$\,236.45 \\ -\,118.19 \end{array}$$

Ⓕ $122.34

Ⓖ $18.26

Ⓗ $118.26

Ⓙ $128.36

4

$20\overline{)6,000}$

Ⓕ 200

Ⓖ 3,000

Ⓗ 3,300

Ⓙ 300

Name _____

1 The standard numeral for the Roman numeral **MDLV** is:

Ⓐ 555 Ⓒ 1,555

Ⓑ 2,605 Ⓓ 960

2 50% is equivalent to what decimal and fraction?

Ⓕ 0.50 and $\frac{1}{2}$ Ⓗ 0.05 and $\frac{1}{2}$

Ⓖ 0.50 and $\frac{50}{10}$ Ⓙ 0.05 and $\frac{50}{1000}$

3 $0.12\overline{)24}$

Ⓐ 2

Ⓑ 200

Ⓒ 0.2

Ⓓ 20

Ⓔ none of these

4 What is the estimated answer?

$ 2.95
  4.05
+ 3.11

Ⓕ $9.00

Ⓖ $11.00

Ⓗ $12.00

Ⓙ $8.00

Ⓚ none of these

187

Name _____

1

$4)\overline{\$8.84}$

Ⓐ $2.02
Ⓑ $2.01
Ⓒ $2.21
Ⓓ $2.31

3 Grandfather caught 4 fish that weighed a total of 12 pounds. What was the average weight of each fish?

Ⓐ 3 lb   Ⓒ 4 lb
Ⓑ 6 lb   Ⓓ 2 lb

2

$$\begin{array}{r} 561 \\ 84 \\ + 327 \\ \hline \end{array}$$

Ⓕ 962
Ⓖ 972
Ⓗ 982
Ⓙ 1,072

4

$$\begin{array}{r} 7\frac{3}{8} \\ - 1\frac{1}{8} \\ \hline \end{array}$$

Ⓕ $6\frac{1}{2}$ Ⓗ $8\frac{1}{2}$

Ⓖ $6\frac{3}{8}$ Ⓙ $6\frac{1}{4}$

188

1 **Use the commutative property to answer the problem below.**

$$3 \times 2 = 2 \times \square$$

Ⓐ 6 Ⓒ 5

Ⓑ 7 Ⓓ 3

2

$$3\overline{)\$9.63}$$

Ⓕ $3.21

Ⓖ $3.12

Ⓗ $3.02

Ⓙ $2.53

3

$$\frac{5}{6} - \frac{1}{6} =$$

Ⓐ $\frac{4}{0}$ Ⓒ $\frac{2}{3}$

Ⓑ $\frac{1}{2}$ Ⓓ $\frac{1}{3}$

4

$$\begin{array}{r} 6 \text{ hr } 10 \text{ min} \\ - 2 \text{ hr } 30 \text{ min} \\ \hline \end{array}$$

Ⓕ 4 hr 20 min Ⓗ 3 hr 80 min

Ⓖ 3 hr 40 min Ⓙ 4 hr 40 min

189

❶

$$\begin{array}{r} 4.25 \\ \times\ \ 1.6 \\ \hline \end{array}$$

Ⓐ 6.78

Ⓑ 6.80

Ⓒ 67.8

Ⓓ 68

❷

$20\overline{)200}$

Ⓕ 10

Ⓖ 102

Ⓗ 100

Ⓙ 12

❸

$$1 \times \frac{1}{3} =$$

Ⓐ $1\frac{1}{3}$

Ⓒ 1

Ⓑ $\frac{1}{3}$

Ⓓ $\frac{2}{3}$

❹

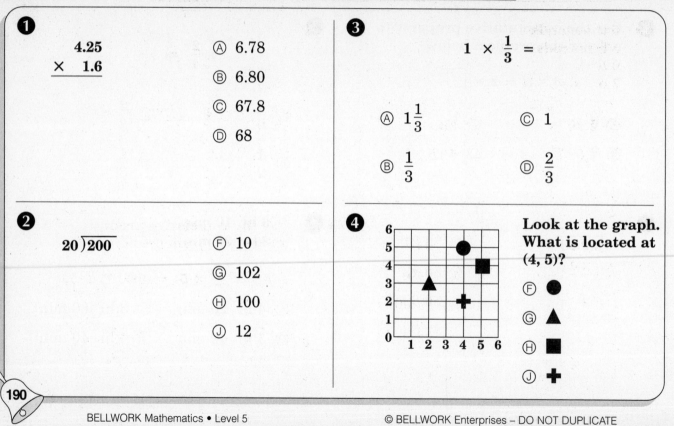

Look at the graph. What is located at (4, 5)?

Ⓕ ●

Ⓖ ▲

Ⓗ ■

Ⓙ ✚

190

1 5 thousands
3 hundreds
0 tens
7 ones =

Ⓐ 5,307 　　Ⓒ 530

Ⓑ 7,035 　　Ⓓ 537

2
$$\begin{array}{r} 4\,2\,0 \\ \times\ \ 2\,0 \\ \hline \end{array}$$

Ⓕ 84

Ⓖ 840

Ⓗ 8,400

Ⓙ 84,000

3
$$\frac{2}{4} = \frac{\square}{8}$$

Ⓐ 2 　　Ⓒ 4

Ⓑ 3 　　Ⓓ 6

4 Use the associative property to answer the problem below.

$$8 \times (\ \square\ \times 5) = (8 \times 7) \times 5$$

Ⓕ 7 　　Ⓗ 15

Ⓖ 13 　　Ⓙ 5

191

1 **What is the prime factorization of 56?**

Ⓐ $2^3 \times 7$ Ⓒ $2 \times 4 \times 7$

Ⓑ 8×7 Ⓓ 1×56

2

$$2 \times \frac{1}{2} =$$

Ⓕ $1\frac{1}{2}$ Ⓗ 1

Ⓖ 2 Ⓙ $\frac{1}{4}$

3 **Find the mean (average) of the following numbers:**

(1.6, 2.7, 3, 3.2, 4.6)

Ⓐ 3 Ⓒ 3.01

Ⓑ 3.02 Ⓓ 30.02

4

$$\begin{array}{r} \$ \ 346.00 \\ - \ 125.68 \\ \hline \end{array}$$

Ⓕ $220.32

Ⓖ $221.42

Ⓗ $221.68

Ⓙ $121.68

Ⓚ none of these

Name _____

❶

$$9.2 - 4.6 =$$

- Ⓐ 5.4
- Ⓒ 13.8
- Ⓑ 4.6
- Ⓓ 5.6

❷

$$236.32 - 14.89 =$$

- Ⓕ 222.57
- Ⓗ 221.53
- Ⓖ 221.43
- Ⓙ 251.21

❸ The first four factors (divisors) of 12 are:

- Ⓐ 0, 1, 2, 3
- Ⓒ 1, 2, 3, 4
- Ⓑ 2, 4, 6, 8
- Ⓓ 12, 24, 36, 48

❹ What is the ratio that does <u>not</u> belong?

$$\boxed{\frac{2}{3}, \frac{6}{9}, \frac{8}{12}, \frac{10}{14}}$$

- Ⓕ $\frac{2}{3}$
- Ⓗ $\frac{8}{12}$
- Ⓖ $\frac{6}{9}$
- Ⓙ $\frac{10}{14}$

Name _____

Look at the different parts of the Venn diagram below and answer the questions that follow.

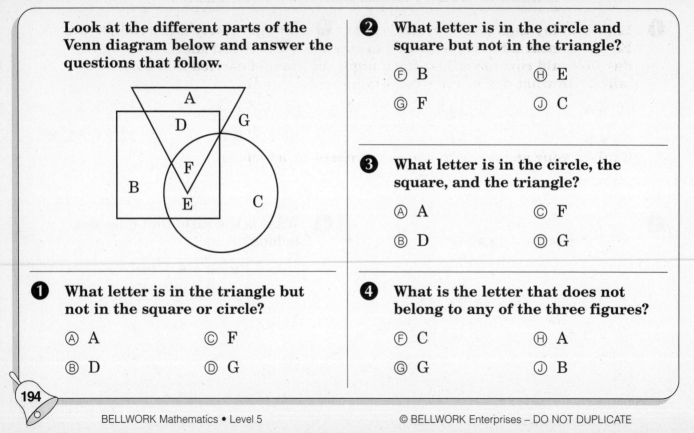

1 What letter is in the triangle but not in the square or circle?

Ⓐ A   Ⓒ F

Ⓑ D   Ⓓ G

2 What letter is in the circle and square but not in the triangle?

Ⓕ B   Ⓗ E

Ⓖ F   Ⓙ C

3 What letter is in the circle, the square, and the triangle?

Ⓐ A   Ⓒ F

Ⓑ D   Ⓓ G

4 What is the letter that does not belong to any of the three figures?

Ⓕ C   Ⓗ A

Ⓖ G   Ⓙ B

Name _____

---

1 Late Monday night, a fisherman's boat ran out of gas thirty miles from shore. Early the next morning he began to row the boat toward shore. During the day he could row ten miles. Each night the current carried him back two miles. On what day of the week did he reach shore?

_____

Explain your answer with words, numbers, or a picture.

1

$$\frac{1}{3} = \frac{\square}{9}$$

Ⓐ 4   Ⓒ 5

Ⓑ 3   Ⓓ 6

3

$$1\frac{1}{4}$$
$$+ \ 2\frac{3}{4}$$

Ⓐ 3   Ⓒ 4

Ⓑ $4\frac{1}{4}$ Ⓓ $3\frac{1}{4}$

2 Cider was sold at the school carnival for 50¢ a cup. 30 quarts of cider were sold. Each quart made 4 cups. How many cups of cider were sold? What information is <u>not</u> needed to solve this problem?

Ⓕ Each quart made 4 cups.

Ⓖ 30 quarts of cider were sold.

Ⓗ Cider was sold for 50¢ a cup.

4

$$12\overline{)360}$$

Ⓕ 300

Ⓖ 30

Ⓗ 291

Ⓙ 36

Name _____

❶

$$2 \overline{)\ \$2.64}$$

 Ⓐ $132.00

 Ⓑ $1.32

 Ⓒ $130.00

 Ⓓ $13.20

 Ⓔ none of these

❷ Which figure is a triangular prism?

Ⓕ

Ⓖ

Ⓗ

Ⓙ

❸ Find the mean (average) of the following numbers:

(6, 6, 14, 2)

Ⓐ 7   Ⓒ 6

Ⓑ 8   Ⓓ 5

❹

$$21.3 \times 2.6 =$$

Ⓕ 5.538   Ⓗ 55.38

Ⓖ 553.8   Ⓙ 0.5538

Name _____

1 **Three multiples of 8 are:**

Ⓐ 8, 10, 12   Ⓒ 1, 2, 4

Ⓑ 8, 16, 24   Ⓓ 8, 12, 20

3 **Which of these is equal to 27?**

Ⓐ 9^3 Ⓒ 3^3

Ⓑ 3^9 Ⓓ 2^5

2 **Kashawnda read $\frac{1}{10}$ of the book. Then she read another $\frac{7}{10}$ of the book. How much did she read altogether?**

Ⓕ $\frac{8}{20}$ Ⓗ $\frac{1}{8}$

Ⓖ $\frac{4}{5}$ Ⓙ $\frac{2}{5}$

4

$$\frac{3}{4} \times 3 =$$

Ⓕ $\frac{3}{4}$ Ⓗ $\frac{6}{4}$

Ⓖ 4   Ⓙ $2\frac{1}{4}$

198

Name _____

❶

$$\frac{2}{4}$$
$$- \frac{1}{3}$$

Ⓐ $\frac{1}{12}$ Ⓒ $\frac{5}{6}$

Ⓑ $\frac{2}{7}$ Ⓓ $\frac{1}{6}$

❸

$$23.9 + 41.21 =$$

Ⓐ 64.11 Ⓒ 65.11

Ⓑ 43.60 Ⓓ 18.12

❷

$$10\overline{)520}$$

Ⓕ 52

Ⓖ 50 R2

Ⓗ 502

Ⓙ 5 R2

❹ **Russ cut 5 oranges into fourths. How many pieces did he make from the 5 oranges?**

Ⓕ 9 pieces Ⓗ 25 pieces

Ⓖ 10 pieces Ⓙ 20 pieces

Name _____

❶

IN	OUT
20	10
	8
12	6
8	4

Look at the table. The missing number is _____.

Ⓐ 22   Ⓒ 16

Ⓑ 14   Ⓓ 18

❸

$$\frac{5}{6} \times 1 =$$

Ⓐ $\frac{5}{6}$ Ⓒ $1\frac{5}{6}$

Ⓑ 6   Ⓓ 1

❷

$$6\frac{7}{8}$$
$$-\ \frac{3}{8}$$

Ⓕ $6\frac{1}{2}$ Ⓗ $\frac{1}{2}$

Ⓖ $7\frac{1}{4}$ Ⓙ $6\frac{5}{8}$

❹ Which number is sixty thousand, four hundred twenty-eight?

Ⓕ 64,428   Ⓗ 6,428

Ⓖ 60,428   Ⓙ 600,428

Name _____

The graph below shows the average monthly temperature in Indianapolis, Indiana. Use the graph to answer the questions that follow.

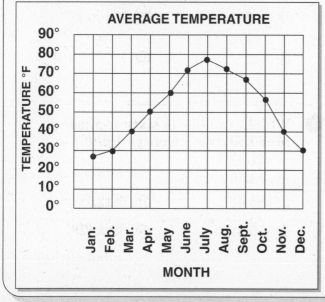

AVERAGE TEMPERATURE

TEMPERATURE °F

MONTH

1 In what month is the average temperature the highest?

ⓐ May   © June

ⓑ July   ⓓ August

2 In what month is the average temperature the lowest?

ⓕ December   ⓗ January

ⓖ February   ⓙ March

3 What is the average temperature in March?

ⓐ 30°   © 40°

ⓑ 35°   ⓓ 50°

4 In what months is the average temperature 40° or below?

ⓕ Jan., Feb., Mar.   ⓗ Feb., Nov., Dec.

ⓖ Mar., Nov., Dec.   ⓙ Jan., Feb., Dec.

201

Name _____

1 On Monday, Cade drove 3.2 miles to the ballpark and spent $8.50 at the game. Then he drove 4.6 miles to the drugstore and spent $6.43. How much money did he spend on Monday?

Ⓐ $14.93

Ⓒ $19.53

Ⓑ $22.73

Ⓓ $7.80

2

$$\frac{1}{3}$$
$$+ \frac{2}{4}$$

Ⓕ $\frac{3}{4}$

Ⓗ $\frac{3}{7}$

Ⓖ $\frac{11}{12}$

Ⓙ $\frac{5}{6}$

3 Which list has <u>only</u> multiples of 7?

Ⓐ 1, 7

Ⓒ 7, 14, 21

Ⓑ 7, 10, 15

Ⓓ 7, 17, 27

4

$$\begin{array}{r} \$\ 26.83 \\ 47.37 \\ +\ 18.50 \end{array}$$

Ⓕ $92.60

Ⓖ $92.50

Ⓗ $92.70

Ⓙ $91.70

Ⓚ none of these

1 On one spin of the spinner, the probability it will stop on D is:

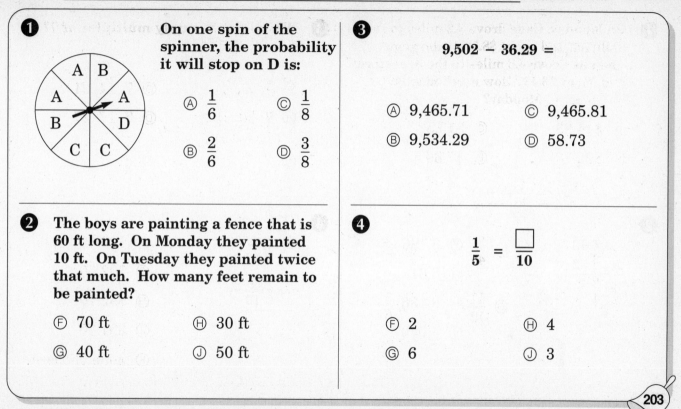

Ⓐ $\frac{1}{6}$

Ⓒ $\frac{1}{8}$

Ⓑ $\frac{2}{6}$

Ⓓ $\frac{3}{8}$

3 $9,502 - 36.29 =$

Ⓐ 9,465.71

Ⓒ 9,465.81

Ⓑ 9,534.29

Ⓓ 58.73

2 The boys are painting a fence that is 60 ft long. On Monday they painted 10 ft. On Tuesday they painted twice that much. How many feet remain to be painted?

Ⓕ 70 ft

Ⓗ 30 ft

Ⓖ 40 ft

Ⓙ 50 ft

4 $\frac{1}{5} = \frac{\square}{10}$

Ⓕ 2

Ⓗ 4

Ⓖ 6

Ⓙ 3

❶

$$2\overline{)\$24.68}$$

Ⓐ $102.34

Ⓑ $12.34

Ⓒ $10.23

Ⓓ $123.40

❸

$$\dfrac{\boxed{}}{4} = 1$$

Ⓐ 4

Ⓒ 8

Ⓑ 2

Ⓓ $\dfrac{1}{4}$

❷

$$\begin{array}{r} 4,068 \\ \times \quad 2 \\ \hline \end{array}$$

Ⓕ 8,126

Ⓖ 8,811

Ⓗ 8,136

Ⓙ 4,070

❹

$$\begin{array}{r} 9\dfrac{6}{10} \\ -\ \dfrac{1}{10} \\ \hline \end{array}$$

Ⓕ $9\dfrac{7}{10}$ Ⓗ $8\dfrac{1}{2}$

Ⓖ $9\dfrac{1}{2}$ Ⓙ 7

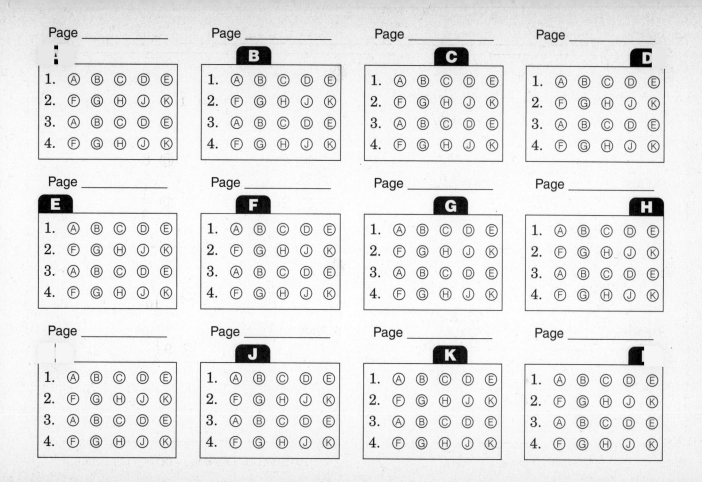

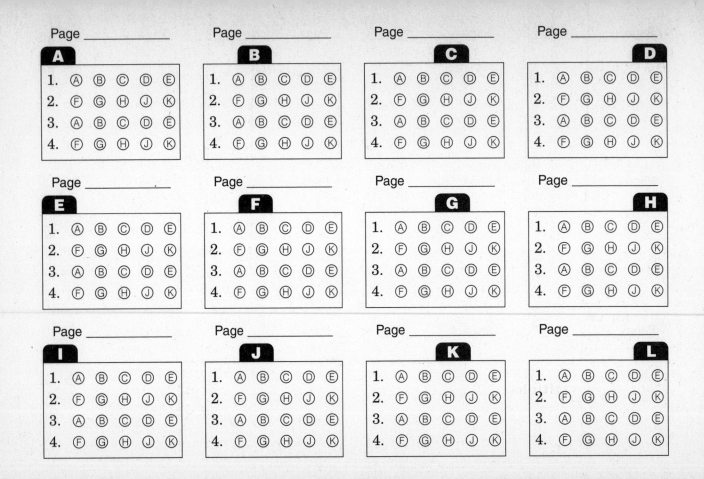